From The Dark Side of The Rainbow

From The Dark Side of The Rainbow

For my wonderful children, John Jr., Timothy, Kimberly, and Christopher, and for their spouses.

I proudly raised them in the land of the free and the home of the brave. They inherited their love and free spirit from their mother and their honor, goodness, and decency from their father, who never had an enemy in his lifetime.

His children forever carry on the bright colors of our rainbow.

—Christina Christy

From The Dark Side of The Rainbow

Caleb Pirtle III

Published by
McLennan House, Inc.
206 South Rogers
Waxahachie, Texas 75165

Library of Congress Cataloging-in-Publication Data
Pirtle III, Caleb, 1941–
FROM THE DARK SIDE OF THE RAINBOW
I. Title
ISBN 0-918865-07-7
Library of Congress Catalog Number: 86-62295

Manufactured in the United States of America
First Printing

Love seeketh not itself to please
Nor for itself hath any care.
But for another gives its ease,
And builds a Heaven in Hell's despair.
                        —William Blake
                        "The Clod and the Pebble"

Prologue

CHRISTINA CHRISTY KEPT HER EYE ON THE FLAG, and her gaze did not waver. She sought strength from it. For so long before, her strength had come from the quiet, reserved sailor who lay in the silver, gray coffin beneath the folds of the red, white, and blue. Christina held her head high, and there were no tears left to stain her cheek.

The preacher's words slurred together and were whipped away by the gulf winds that blew cold and damp across the Houston, Texas, cemetery. They were meant for her. But Christina Christy no longer heard them. She shivered as the February chill cut through her black dress, and the impetuous smile that could find a trace of humor in any situation, no matter how tragic, had faded. Her eyes had become as gray as her last day on earth with the remains of John Christy.

The eulogy spoke of love and honor, duty and devotion. To Christina, John symbolized them all.

So did the flag, and Christina could not remove her eyes from the stars and the stripes that fluttered only a few feet away from her. John was lying so close, and yet she would never feel his arms around her again when times were hard, and times had been so hard, and they would have been unbearable without him. Christina felt so empty, so alone. She wondered why the tears would no longer come, and deep inside she knew.

She was a sea captain's wife, now his widow, and she squared her fragile shoulders with pride and a fierce independence that John had sometimes cursed but always admired.

Christina had been his wife, his mistress, his lover, his friend, the mother of his four children.

The sea had been John's life. Always it had beckoned to him. Always he had heard the tides of a distant shore call his name. And he had followed. Being the master of a ship was what he knew how to do. It was what he did best. It was his dream fulfilled.

John would be gone for weeks, sometimes for months. Christina often felt a great rage boiling up within her, a contempt for the oceans that kept them apart, that cradled him at night when her bed was empty. John Christy knew the sea better than any thing or any one, even her. The sea was his temptress.

But he always came back to Christina.

That had been her salvation during those long, lonesome months when she watched the seasons change as slowly she grew older without him. Christina had spent so much of her life with John, yet the sea always kept him just beyond her reach. Perhaps the sea was as jealous as she. It had finally called to him for the last time.

The sea had brought John Christy to her.

Now it had taken him away.

Christina watched as the honor guard slowly and methodically, by the numbers, lifted the flag from the coffin and began to fold it as they had done so many times before, strangers paying tribute to a man they didn't know. Grief was never a stranger. It followed everywhere they went, as much a part of them as the flag.

Their faces were solemn, hidden in the quick, regimented shadow of their movements, their backs rigid and straight. John would have approved of them, Christina thought. He firmly believed that anything worth doing was worth doing right. He demanded discipline from his crew. He earned their respect. They loved him as he loved the sea. John Christy was tough, but fair. He was a professional. He made few mistakes.

He was at home on the sea.

Now the sea had claimed him.

His tanker, the *V.A. Fogg,* had docked at Freeport to unload 123,000 barrels of highly-combustible benzene, then sailed at 1:30 P.M. on February 1, 1972, still carrying 19,000 barrels of xylene.

The *Fogg* was pointed toward the open sea, heading somewhere fifty to a hundred miles offshore to clean her tanks before turning back to Galveston and home. It was a task that John Christy had done so many times in the past. His voyage at last was beyond him, mission accomplished. Those long, empty weeks at sea were almost behind him. Christina, his lovely Krischia, would be waiting. John Christy was grinning broadly as he looked eastward while the Texas coastline faded into the light mist that dropped from the February sky.

No one would ever hear from John Christy again. His radios were silent. His ship simply disappeared, there on the horizon, then suddenly gone, taking thirty-nine good men with it.

At 4:10 P.M. that afternoon, a NASA pilot flying a T-38 trainer reported seeing a ball of fire and smoke rising to a ceiling of ten thousand feet about sixty-five miles south of Galveston. It was a mushroom-shaped cloud, and he at first feared that he had witnessed a nuclear explosion. Later, he thought that perhaps it was a volcano erupting out of the Gulf of Mexico. Frankly, the pilot didn't know what he had seen, but the smoke boiling up from water below had left him shaken.

The *V.A. Fogg*, according to responsible calculations, was due to arrive at the sea buoy off the end of Galveston's rock jetties at two o'clock in the darkness of Wednesday morning. It was a clear night. The waters were calm. No one was worried.

In her modest Colonial brick home in southeast Houston, Christina awoke suddenly and stared at the clock. John was late. He always called her as soon as he came ashore, saying simply, "Here I am. Come and get me."

John hadn't called, and outside her bedroom window, the darkness was streaked with the first faint traces of daylight. Christina rubbed the sleep from her concerned eyes, leaned against John's pillow, and stared at the telephone, waiting for it to ring and tell her John was home safe again.

Silence.

Hours of silence.

Then it rang. The voice was soft and reassuring, but it was not a familiar one. Its message was brief and to the point: "The *V.A. Fogg* is missing."

By midmorning, Coast Guard cutters were plowing their way through a calm sea, searching for some trace, some sign—any sign—of the 572-foot tanker. It could not simply have vanished. It was much too large and much too close to port. Aircraft circled overhead. The day dragged on.

The sea was empty.

Late in the afternoon, a cutter picked up a burnt orange kapok life jacket. That was all.

Three days later, a plank was found adrift, and upon it had been stenciled the name: *V.A. Fogg*. Floating nearby was a fiberglass life raft container, a life ring, and a door.

Slowly, almost selfishly, in bits and pieces the sea was beginning to give back the ship it had taken.

Christina haunted the hallways of the Coast Guard station night and day. She refused to leave. There was no place else for her to go. "Here is where it all began for me," she said, her voice flat and drained of emotion. "And here is where it will end."

She felt as though she were living on a swinging pendulum and couldn't get off. She struggled to hang on to those last threads of hope although she could feel them beginning to unravel in her hands. Christina walked the rock jetties, staring at the sea, cursing it because the gulf would not give forth its secret. At first she had been frightened, waiting for someone, anyone, to tell her what had happened, frustrated because nobody could, gripped by the anxiety, the fear of the unknown. Was John hurt? Christina doubted it. Was he dead? Probably. But she didn't know for sure, and it was the uncertainty that tormented her every waking hour, and Christina could not sleep. She kept reaching for him, and her fingers touched only the past.

There was no reason for John Christy to have even been aboard the *V.A. Fogg* that Tuesday. He had been scheduled to come ashore at Freeport, but his relief captain hadn't been feeling well, and John urged him to remain in port, volunteering to take the tanker on back to Galveston himself.

John was like that.

He always gave of himself.

This time he had given his life.

In a Houston newspaper, Christina had read the words of Leo Blacton who had served as John's third mate on a previous voyage of the *V.A. Fogg*. Blacton had told a reporter for the *Chronicle*,

I've been going to sea since World War II. I've been on lots of ships, but never with a better crew than the *Fogg*. The harmony and cooperation between these men were phenomenal. They were all such gentlemen.

Christina forced a smile. John was certainly an officer and a gentleman. But where was he, and what had happened to him?

Only the sea knew. The sea would tell no one. Christina sat and watched the waves come sweeping in to touch the shore then turn away again. The Gulf of Mexico was cold, and its waters dark. Eleven days had passed, and all that had been recovered was a survival kit and a ten-man life raft. Like the sea, it, too, was empty.

Perhaps John had known he could not beat the deep waters forever, she thought. He understood the dangers, but he never dwelled on them. Yet Christina could not forget the Christmas card he had sent his friends barely two months ago. It was a different kind of card, one so untypical of John. Its message said simply:

O Lord,
Thy sea is
so great
and
my boat
is so small.

At the time, Christina thought it an odd greeting to mail out to friends. John only smiled when she questioned him about it. Now, she thought, maybe it hadn't been a greeting at all. Maybe it had been a farewell.

As the late evening shadows wound their way among the whitecaps like purple ribbons, Christina recalled their trip to Switzerland only a summer before. She hadn't thought so much about it then, but now it was obvious to her. It had seemed to her that she and John were trying hard to catch up with their lives. It was as though he had known that life was running out.

Those were days and nights, especially the nights, when he held her close and whispered her name and made her forget those long months they spent apart, that she prayed would never end.

They had.

She didn't want to believe it, yet she knew it was true. Christina ached for him, and, alone on the rock jetties, she no longer had to wear the stone face of a sea captain's wife who never bowed nor broke when trouble surrounded her. She could be what she was, a wife, a woman.

And she wept.

And the gentle Texas winds dried her tears.

On the twelfth day, Christina Christy gave up hope.

John Christy's memorial service was held on the chilly afternoon of February 13, in the Zion Lutheran Church of Pasadena, Texas. Christina had hoped it would give her peace, but there was no peace, only a nightmare from which there would be no awakening. She sat there, her children at her side, and she kept thinking: I have no coffin to touch, no grave to visit. John's not here. He's still at sea. This time he didn't come back to me. He's never coming back. I will go to the end of the seawall to sit and hope he hears me. He always has before. But then, he's always come home before.

In the late hour of the day, when the crowds had gone, leaving her alone again, Christina Christy returned to the rock jetties, a spray of flowers in her hand. She paused, closed her eyes as if in prayer, then smiled as those distant memories of love and happiness came to comfort her as the last remnants of twilight ushered in the night. The only sounds she heard were the crashing of the whitecaps against the rocks below her and the sometimes frantic, sometimes mournful cries of the seagulls that rode the winds above. Christina trembled, and a cold stillness slowly crept over her. She knelt and tossed the flowers into the water, hoping they would find John and float to where the corpse of his ship lay buried.

The next day, a team of six divers found the wreckage of the *V.A. Fogg* lying in ninety feet of water, fifty miles to the southeast of Galveston. There were, as everyone suspected, no survivors.

The tanker, investigators concluded, had exploded like a string of firecrackers, with blasts strong enough to blow out both sides of the vessel. One-inch thick steel plates were ripped apart like pieces of scrap paper. Seams buckled, and pipes were twisted like spaghetti. There were gaping holes in the hull of the *V.A. Fogg.*

It had sunk within three minutes, without a cry for help. There had not been time.

Divers returned to shore with only one body, found adrift and intact in the *Fogg's* chart room.

John Christy had come home at last.

Above the wreckage, the *SS William T. Steele* anchored in the waves, and the ship's master, H.H. Mathies, looked down at the gulf and said with a loud, yet cracked voice, "I now consign the remains of these men to their final resting place in the deep, to remain there until the day of final judgement when the sea shall give up her dead."

There were four prolonged blasts from the vessel's whistle, and a floral tribute was dropped onto the surface of the water.

No one else had been found.

Only John Christy had returned.

Christina reached and took the folded flag that the Honor Guard was holding out to her. She at last had her coffin to touch, a grave to visit. The nightmare had ended, and now the sadness, the solitude could begin. At least the uncertainty of it all was gone, and for that Christina could be thankful.

She held the flag tightly against her breasts as Christina walked back toward her waiting limousine. The flag, Old Glory. It meant everything to her. She had adopted it and the country over which it so proudly flew. For her, America had indeed been the land of the free at a time when she had never known freedom.

It hadn't belonged to her.

Christina had stolen it.

Christina would have done anything to be with John, even break the law, and she had.

He was her savior. He had given her a reason to live when the tragedies of war had destroyed her will to live. Her world had been so bleak, so empty, so worthless. John had become her anchor in the midst of a storm that had threatened to ruin her as surely as it had ruined her homeland.

He had held her and kissed her, had gently taken her arm and led her back from the dark side of the rainbow.

Chapter 1

THE CITY BELOW HER lay dying.

Christina Skiba slowly, almost haltingly, made her way back down the rocky slope of Gellert Hill, watching as long, bony fingers of night crept into the alleyways of Budapest. Soon the streets would be empty, and people would be hiding in the darkness behind locked doors again, waiting and wondering, never quite sure of what each new day would bring them. Their spirits were as broken as the ancient church spires that had once stood so tall, so proud above the city. Now they had crumbled, and the towers that had pointed toward God were rubble in the gutter, crushed beneath the tanks that had rumbled into Budapest like great, armored angels of death.

At least the shelling had stopped, and an ominous silence stalked both banks of the Danube, still beautiful amidst the ravages of war. Its waters had been stained by the blood of good men who fought and died, not for a cause, but for the hope of their own preservation. The stench of their death had hung like a warm winter's mist over Budapest long after the staccato of gunfire, the thunder of cannonfire had ceased, leaving the city to mourn its dead and comfort the worn, troubled souls of its survivors.

From the crest of Gellert Hill, the agony of war seemed so far away. Christina Skiba found peace there, hiking alone in the quiet of a summer afternoon, her eyes closed, listening as the birds sang of better days when no one was frightened or would ever be frightened again. She smiled and ran her slender fingers through her hair, a dark brown unruly mass of curls, and tried to force the bitter memories of the dead and the dying from her mind, walking faster now, trying to outrun the shadows of twilight, aware that she must beat the night home.

Christina had come to Budapest as an impetuous child of twelve, eager to spend the final days of summer with her Aunt Vera and Uncle Arpad. It was a holiday that she had been long awaiting. It would become a nightmare. Christina, when she first climbed among the trees to the top of the hill, didn't have a care in the world. Her days were full of laughter, and she was as free as the yellow butterfly that caught the wind with its outstretched wings and flew everywhere and nowhere, but mostly in her aunt's garden of cornflowers.

There was no reason for Christina to worry. She was young and independent, a blithe spirit who had been terribly spoiled by her mother and father. She was the only child in her whole family, someone special, and all of her aunts showered her with the devotion and affection they had saved for the children they never had.

Christina had mischief in her eyes. She did what she wanted to do and generally got away with it.

Her own father had been a White Russian Baron, and Christina could feel that aristocratic blood running wild through her veins. But he had died when she was a babe, had broken his neck after falling from his horse in a mad dash across the meadows outside of Lublin, and she had no memories of those strong, genteel hands picking her up and holding her high into the sunlight for all to see. Christina knew him only through the stories her mother told, and she didn't mention him much at all after marrying Pavel Skiba, perhaps the most respected pharmacist in all of Bydgoszcz. Without hesitation, her mother's new husband adopted Christina, not because he felt any responsibility for her, but simply because he loved her and would raise her as his own. His would be the face she always saw when she dreamed of home.

Even when home had been lost and was a war away.

For Christina, it was far beyond her reach but never beyond her thoughts, even when bombs rattled the floors of her uncle's house and lit up the night with the lightning brilliance of a resurrection morning.

As the long, hot summer of 1939 dragged slowly to an end, Christina packed her satchel and made plans to board the train that would carry her back to her hometown of Bydgoszcz again. She and her mother had been ticketed to travel together, but a sudden intestinal virus had stricken Christina, leaving her too weak and nauseous to face those hours after merciless hours on the rails.

She remembered her mother smiling, even though worry had furrowed deep into her brow. A cool, soft hand had reached down to brush aside the tangled curls that were plastered with sweat against Christina's forehead.

Elizabeth Skiba sat there for a long time without speaking, only smiling that sad smile of her's, dreading those incessant ticks of the clock that were pulling her away from her daughter.

"I hate to leave you," she said softly, "but your papa needs me back at the pharmacy. I promised him I would be back today, and you know how he worries so when I'm late."

"Yes, mama."

The fever had broken slightly, and Christina's stomach didn't throb nearly so badly as before. All night she had felt faint, and the dull ache had made it almost impossible to sleep. She had vomited about three-fifteen, according to the antique, mahogany clock at the far end of the hallway, and then again shortly before daylight, and her mother sadly made the decision to leave her daughter behind. The trip she knew, would be nerve-racking and arduous, and she couldn't stand the thought of Christina throwing up on some businessman with appointments, perhaps, in Berlin—or in some other major city between Budapest and Bydgoszcz. It was best for her daughter to remain with Aunt Vera until she regained her strength, Elizabeth Skiba told herself. She was sure of it.

"I'll call you when I get home to see how you're doing," she said, forcing a smile she didn't feel in her heart. "In a few days you should be feeling much better, and Uncle Arpad can take you down to the depot and make sure you catch the right train home."

"Yes, mama."

Christina turned her face away and found herself staring at the pale green walls of her Aunt's guest bedroom. The plaster had cracked beneath the paint, but she had to look close to see it, and a ray of sunlight had fallen through the shadows and gotten caught in a dusty web that some spider had long ago abandoned.

Christina felt lost. She already missed her mother terribly, and Elizabeth Skiba wasn't even gone.

"Mama?"

"Yes, dear."

"I'm feeling a lot better already." Christina struggled to sit up in bed, leaning against her goose-down pillow for support. "I can come with you. I don't have to wait."

Elizabeth hugged her daughter and gently brushed aside the tears that had moistened her dark eyes. "I don't think we'd be wise to chance that," she replied.

"I know for sure I'd be well tomorrow." There was a plea in the girl's voice.

"I pray that you will."

"Wait until tomorrow to go, mama."

Elizabeth stood and straightened the wrinkles that had creased her blue dress. "You know I can't do that, Krischia," she said sternly. "I have already explained to you that papa is expecting me back today, and there is much work to be done, and he needs me to help him do it."

Christina nodded, her eyes downcast.

"Aunt Vera will take good care of you, and I want you to be a good little patient."

"Yes, mama."

"And Krischia . . ."

"Yes, mama."

"I don't want to see you crying when I leave." She leaned over and kissed her daughter lightly on the cheek. Again those cool, gentle hands wiped away the flecks of perspiration from the girl's flushed face. Christina, she must have thought, looked so small lying there, so pale and helpless. There was the look of a frightened animal in her eyes, and Elizabeth quickly turned away, feeling uneasy about her decision to leave.

"Mama?"

"Yes, dear."

"I love you."

"I love you, too, dear." Elizabeth glanced at the clock in the hallway and realized that she had run out of time. She couldn't linger any longer. The train out of Budapest waited for no one. She sighed, and continued, "Now be a good little girl, Krischia. Do what your Aunt Vera asks you to do, take your medicine when you're told, get well in a hurry, and I'll be there to meet you when you get back home."

"Yes, mama."

"And Krischia, don't cry after I'm gone."

"No, mama."

Christina saw her mother smile for the last time, pick up her quilted bag, and quietly slip through the door, gently closing it behind her.

"Bye, mama," she whispered.

From down the hallway she heard the big front door slam shut, and Christina caught her breath. She turned, tore the dusty spider web away from the green plaster wall, and buried her small face in the soft down of her Aunt Vera's pillow.

But she didn't cry.

She felt nauseous again, homesick, alone, weak, and a sharp pain jabbed at the pit of her stomach. But Christina didn't cry. She kept her promises. She always had. And the room spun until she closed her eyes to make it stop.

When she awoke, it was dark outside and very still. Not even the winds were blowing, and the suffocating heat of summer lingered in the room and draped itself like a scratchy woolen shawl around Christina's shoulders. She wondered what time it was and if her mother's train had reached Bydgoszcz yet and guessed that it probably had.

Christina crawled from beneath the wrinkled sheet that was wet with perspiration and stumbled across the unfamiliar bedroom floor to the window. Beyond the white linen curtain, she could see a narrow, deserted street winding as it had for centuries past a row of old but neatly-kept stone cottages, barely visible in the darkness that reached down around them. Before, it had always been such a friendly street, leading her to the parks and fountains that were scattered throughout Budapest and on to Gellert Hill. There Christina would sit for hours just outside the great walls of the Citadel, her imagination running wild as she thought of the days when those grim-faced troops from Vienna stood on the terrace, keeping watch over a fanatical band of Hungarian Rebels who thirsted after and would die for their independence. But now the street was empty and forlorn, much like Christina herself. Even the lamps, burning in the distance, were not as bright as usual.

Outside, it was so quiet, so calm, so peaceful.

Why, then, was she so sad?

Christina didn't know. Her mother was gone, but her mother had left her before. She was only a girl, yet she was twelve and already showed early signs of looks that would one day blossom into full womanhood. The stomach virus had weakened her, but the fever was gone and the dull ache had subsided sometime during the night, and she was craving food again, and that, she decided, must be a sign that she was getting better. The ache had left her stomach, but it had lodged in her heart, and Christina felt that somewhere, something was dreadfully wrong, and she didn't know what, and that began to frighten her.

It wasn't the night.

Christina had never been afraid of the night.

She looked down and her hands were trembling, and she grabbed the windowsill to steady them. Her breath came in short, spasmodic bursts, and a cold stillness crept over her.

"Mama, I love you," Christina said to herself.

She was the only one who heard.

She knelt and leaned against the open window, letting a faint breeze blow warm against her face. She stared out into the darkness but saw no sign of life anywhere. The whole world was asleep, she decided. Only she, Christina Skiba, would be awake to welcome the new day when it arrived. Perhaps she was the only one who waited so impatiently to see daylight again. It was important to her. Each sunrise would bring her one day closer to being home again.

The minutes crawled past.

The clock lost its interest in ticking.

A cloud blotted out the full summer moon, and Christina watched the shadows creep slowly down the street below her, inching their way back into the alleyways as silently, as stealthily as a black cat in the night.

The countryside, as far as she could see, was forsaken, devoid of life.

Beyond her vision, and across two countries, there were figures—thousands of them—moving through the darkness, swarming over the wooded hillsides, dragging ominous, metallic instruments of death and destruction behind them. The night hid them and muted their voices. The sounds of their footsteps, the angry rattle of those instruments of death fell on deaf ears, unsuspecting and sleeping.

One man stood apart and alone. The brass on his hat, the brass of authority, glittered in the moonlight as he watched those figures, tall and young with blackened faces, move obediently into place as he had ordered. He glanced at his watch then toward the sky.

He had his orders.

He, too, was waiting for daylight.

The forest was filled with figures scrambling for their positions, the quietness punctuated by grunts and curses and an occasional shout that interfered with the solace of the night. The instruments of death were turned and pointed across empty fields where farmers had toiled to grow, then harvest, the crops that would keep their families fed during the cold, frost-bitten days ahead.

The fields had given them life.

Across them would come the footsteps of their appointed executioners, eyes hardened and trained to look without pity nor conscience past the trail of death that they would leave behind them.

The man with the brass on his hat saw the first streaks of dawn that pierced the eastern horizon, just above the tree line, and his jaws tightened. Everyone by now must be in place, he knew. There could be no mistakes. There could be no miscalculations. Berlin would not stand for it. He managed a tightlipped smile and turned his attention to the unguarded, unprotected borders of Poland.

The rising sun would bring a brave, new day, he told himself, a glorious new day.

The Third Reich was counting on him.

He would not fail them.

A funereal hush fell across the wooded hillsides as daylight yawned, then spilled cautiously out across the deserted Polish farmlands.

Cannonfire roared like thunder from a surprised and cloudless sky. Men died before they were ever awakened. Women screamed and hid their faces in terror as the metallic instruments of death sent shells slamming into the soft, fertile ground around them. Children were blown away, and families torn apart, and blood seeped into the plant rows, staining the earth that one day would hold too many graves beneath too many tombstones that bore no names.

The morning of September 1, 1939, began with horror.

The well-oiled machinery of a superbly-armed German Army stormed across the borders of Poland while, in Berlin, the unblinking, maddened eyes of the Fuehrer stared at a war map, coldly contemplating the invasion, the fall, and the annihilation of the Polish people.

The sun was just beginning its climb across the broad German sky.

The battle, Adolph Hitler knew, had already been launched if all went according to plan, and he could afford no delays. He would strike, strike quickly, and strike with force, and all of Europe would tremble before him. He sat back, closed his eyes, and a sneer creased his face. Word from the front would be coming soon, and he waited to bask in the glow of the victory that must be won.

Christina shuddered.

Dawn had found her still leaning against the window, her eyes turned toward home, a hollow feeling of uneasiness rippling through her slim body. The sun danced behind an early-morning mist, and the gentle winds were cool and refreshing against her face, parched and dried out by the fever. She slowly arose and shed her night clothes, reaching for the new, starched dress that she was to have worn back to Bydgoszcz. Christina held it for a moment, then carefully placed it across the foot of her wrinkled bedsheet. She would wear an older dress today, Christina told herself, and save the new one for the train ride tomorrow. She would stay in Budapest no longer than tomorrow, and that was a promise, and she forced a smile, knowing that she always kept her promises.

Christina quickly ran a brush through her curls and hummed to herself as she skipped down the hallway to the breakfast room. It would be a beautiful day after all, she decided, and she was famished. For once, Christina didn't even mind hanging around the kitchen to watch her Aunt Vera prepare the meal.

She noticed that her Uncle Arpad wore a worried frown and spent most of the day bent over a small radio, trying desperately to sort through the words that finally squeezed their way through the static. He said little, but he and Aunt Vera kept exchanging concerned looks, and there was no laughter during lunch and no supper at all.

Christina felt that tinge of fright begin to boil up within her again. The house was full of whispers, and outside, men were late for work or they didn't go at all. They gathered on street corners, and there was anger and disgust in their voices, and beside the Lanchid Suspension Bridge, Christina saw an old man crying, and it troubled her because Christina had never seen a grown man cry before. He just stood there, his shoulders slumped, his head against the rock column, wrenching his old rag cap in his hands while tears flowed shamelessly down his tired, whiskered face.

What had happened? Christina grew confused.

What had gone wrong?

She had asked her uncle, but he only patted her on the shoulder in a patronizing sort of way and walked out of the room without saying a word.

The radio grew louder as the voices grew weaker, and Christina saw that Uncle Arpad's ruddy complexion had become ashen. His eyes were pale and had lost their twinkle. His fists were clenched as though he wanted to strike out at something or someone and didn't quite know what or who to hit. Frustration was obviously eating away at him, and Christina stayed out of his way. Aunt Vera didn't go out all day. Christina returned to her room early, closing her door and packing her suitcase again.

Feared gnawed at her, and still she didn't know why.

She only wanted to be home.

Now.

Not tomorrow.

Now. She ached to feel her father's strong arms around her. Christina thought back to the night of the storm last spring when the winds howled about the house and sheared the roof away. A crack of thunder had awakened her, so close that she could feel the room shake, and the thunder rumbled inside her chest like a kettle drum. Lightning seemed to bounce against her window, and the panes rattled until they broke. One moment, Christina was dry, scared but dry. And the next, she was drenched. The roof was gone as quick as a lightning bolt, and torrents of angry rain pounded down upon her. At first, she thought she was drowning and could hardly breathe, but suddenly her father was there, bending over her, holding her tightly, shielding her from the rain with his own back.

"It's all right, Krischia," he had said.

"I'm scared." Her voice was trembling and far away.

"Don't worry. I'm here with you now."

"Don't leave me, papa."

"I won't, Krischia. You're my little girl. I won't ever leave you."

Where was her father now?

Christina closed the suitcase and fastened it. She put on her fresh, starched traveling dress, gave up trying to brush the curls that were plastered like ringlets against her head, and walked slowly down the hallway toward the big mahogany clock. It was seven-fifteen and almost fully dark outside.

Christina had no idea when the next train would be departing for Bydgoszcz.

She only knew that she wanted to be on it.

She stepped timidly inside the living room, standing thin and frail in the doorway, nervously fiddling with the handle of her case. For a moment, no one saw her. Uncle Arpad was hammering the radio with his fist in an effort to clear up the static and catch every morsel of news that was being broadcast across the continent. And to Christina, each new word seemed to have aged him. She had never seen his spirit so broken before.

Aunt Vera was simply sitting by herself in the corner and staring at the picture of her family that hung on the far wall above the sofa. It was, she had told friends, her most prized possession, with, of course, the exception of Arpad. The photograph had been taken on a holiday along the Baltic Sea only two months before her father died. He had always been special to her. So was his picture.

Christina glanced at the photograph she had seen so

many times before. There were her mother, Vera, Sophie, and Jadwega, all sisters, all laughing as though they didn't have a care in the world. In those days, perhaps, they didn't. They were discovering themselves and their place on earth with fresh, young, and innocent eyes. Bad times were only temporary. Good times were forever.

But where had they all gone?

Aunt Vera, as though suddenly aware of the dark, penetrating eyes that were reaching out to her, turned toward Christina as the girl set her suitcase down on the wooden floor with a soft thud.

"What are you doing, child?" she asked.

Christina took a deep breath. "I'm going home," she replied softly.

"You can't."

"I have to."

Aunt Vera glanced painfully at Arpad then looked back toward her niece. She sighed and reached out her right hand, beckoning for Christina to come to her. Her face was drawn with worry. "I have something to tell you," she said, and her eyes shifted away from Christina's gaze.

"Has something happened to mama?"

Aunt Vera shook her head.

"Papa?"

"No, child. They're just fine." Aunt Vera put an arm around Christina's waist and drew her closer. "But you won't be able to go home for awhile."

"Why not?" Christina felt a sudden chill cut through her body.

"Sit down, child, and I'll try to explain it to you." Aunt Vera's voice was drained of emotion. Her words were flat and halting, as though she herself didn't really understand what she was telling the girl. "Poland is at war. It all happened early this morning while we were asleep. For some reason—I don't know why—the German army marched into Poland, and the Polish people are fighting

back, and, right now, I'm afraid the whole country is in an uproar. It's no place for a young girl to be. I know that for a fact."

Bewilderment settled deep in Christina's face. She started to speak, stopped herself, then said sharply, "I must go home. Mama expects me to be there, and so does papa. They need me, and if the train leaves tonight, I can be there before morning."

"It's too dangerous," Uncle Arpad snapped, looking up from his radio, frantically twisting the dials and cursing the static under his breath.

Christina stuck out her chin stubbornly and asked, "Are the Germans in Bydgoszcz?"

"No." Aunt Vera bit her bottom lip in frustration.

"Then it's not too dangerous for me to go home."

"They may be there before the week is out."

"I can beat them. I can get there before they do." Christina pulled away from her aunt and ran across the room, suddenly in a hurry, aware that there was no time to waste and what little time she had left was rapidly running out on her. "I can do it," she said loudly.

"You can't." Aunt Vera was on her feet, screaming now, tears gushing freely from her weary eyes.

"You can't stop me."

"No, I can't." The woman wiped away her tears, and her voice began to quake. "But the Germans can, and believe me, child, they will."

"They have no right to."

"They do what they want," Arpad growled.

Christina sat down abruptly on her suitcase, and she could feel fear beginning to crawl through her again, pricking her skin like needle points. She had been afraid for hours. Now, at last, she knew why.

"I don't understand war," the girl said, nervously fidgeting with the ends of her curls. "I've read about it in my history books and I've studied about it in school, but I don't know why it happens."

"Nobody really does." Aunt Vera sat down again, but not before taking the photograph down from the wall and gingerly brushing away the dust from its glass and gold metallic frame.

"Why are people killed?"

"Because some men are selfish."

"Why was Germany mad at Poland?"

"Germany wasn't," Uncle Arpad interrupted. "It's just that that crazy man running Germany wants everything that doesn't belong to him, and Poland doesn't belong to him, so he marched his army in to take it."

"That's not fair."

"War never is."

"Who's going to stop them?"

Uncle Arpad shrugged his shoulders dejectedly and turned the radio off. The news he was getting was old, and all of it was bad, and his head ached, and he was getting sick to his stomach just thinking about the battle raging across Poland. Poland wasn't even ready for war. Poland didn't even have an army, at least he had never heard anybody talk about one. Christina's question had indeed been a good one. Who was going to stop Hitler. Damned if he knew.

"Have you heard from mama?" Christina asked shyly.

Aunt Vera shook her head.

"Then how do you know that she and papa are all right?"

"I just know, child," Aunt Vera replied. "When you're family, you just know when everything is fine and when it isn't. Right now, your mama and papa are in no danger."

"Can they get out?"

"No. The border is closed."

"And I can't get in." It was a statement, spoken matter-of-factly, with no emotion, that required no answer.

Christina walked slowly, as if in a trance, to the window and looked out upon the city. The men who had gathered on street corners were now going their separate ways, heads bowed, concern etched on waxen faces. Women were herding their children back indoors, and the smell of boiling cabbage wafted from doorway to doorway.

All was so calm.

So peaceful.

It had been the best of times. Now they had been shattered, and Christina felt trapped, and she closed her eyes and desperately tried to remember the smile on her mama's face as she walked out the door that afternoon.

How long had it been?

Only yesterday?

For a moment, Christina thought she would cry, but she caught her breath and straightened her shoulders, watching the last rays of a weary sun painting shadows, purple and orange, on the row of cottages across the street.

"Aunt Vera," she asked, "what will happen to mama and papa?"

Silence.

Christina turned and her eyes blurred. "Will I ever see them again?" It was a question, simple and direct, that fell in silence as darkness again slipped awkwardly into Budapest, much like an Hungarian Gypsy drifter looking for some place, close and warm, to spend the night.

Chapter 2

CHRISTINA TURNED HER BACK ON GELLERT'S HILL and walked quickly toward the banks of the Danube, its waters the color of molten gold in the glow of the setting sun. She looked out across the panorama of the city, once so beautiful, but that was before the cannonfire had crumbled its walls and the bombs had rocked, then splintered its foundations.

The poet Janos Arany had come often to the Corso, the pathway that followed the gently winding shoreline of the river, and he had written with pride and passion of the sights and sounds that lay before him.

As far as Christina was concerned, no one had ever been able to describe the beauty of Budapest as well as Arany. Perhaps no one could. One stanza had particularly lodged in her mind, and it came to her as Christina hurried past the burned-out ruins of the Vigado, the concert hall where music by the masters had enraptured the soul and the staccato of gunfire had destroyed it.

Arany had gazed out across the city from his favorite vantage point, and he had written:

Upon the Danube's bank in Pest I stand,
And see a canvas made by master-hand,
Cloudlets and hilltops notch the azure sky,
While to you City Farm the sun draws nigh.
The Gellert proudly wears its velvet gown,
And on its head the new grief—the new crown!
Down in the Taban standeth forth a spire,
Its golden pommel almost glows with fire.
Above stands Corvine's steeple, dark, sublime,
Admidst the stream of ever flowing time.
The row of houses, in the distance drawn,
Is like white linen, bleaching on the lawn.
Below the mighty river, smooth and sheen,
Is like a tarn in mountains, emerald-green,
Untouched of swallows' wings or wanton air,
It hides a force that lies deep in its lair.
Its surface is a mirror, in it seems
The self-same picture, as in fairy dreams,
New-washed, upside down floating on the wave,
The rigid stone-walls like a carpet wave.

That's the way it had been, the way Christina had first looked upon Budapest so many years ago through the innocent eyes of childhood. Janos Arany had captured it for her. The war had taken it away.

At first, it had only been hearsay, fragmented reports from faraway battlefields, and Christina, at the naive age of twelve, didn't really feel threatened by it at all. It was only a matter of inconvenience, and she waited somewhat impatiently every day for a letter from her mother telling her that it would be all right to come home again. The letter never came.

Uncle Arpad seldom smiled anymore. Headlines in the newspaper kept a worried frown on his face, even when business was good, and no one had become too frightened yet to quit spending good money. The war couldn't last forever, and Hungary had thus far escaped the dreaded Nazi *Blitzkrieg*. Others might be suffering, but life had not changed too radically in Budapest. Perhaps the deadly apocalypse of war would not intrude across the borders of Hungary at all.

Christina lay, late at night, the pangs of loneliness gnawing at her insides. She was safe. At least she felt safe. But she longed to have her mother's arms wrapped around her again, and who, she wondered, would her father take to the sailing races on Sunday afternoon now that she was away? She closed her eyes, and she could almost feel his strong, gentle hand around hers as they walked together along the shoreline of the lake, watching as that fleet of sleek, colorful racing vessels plowed their way gracefully through the water, their glistening white sails reaching up to catch the wayward gusts of a summer wind. Those had been special days.

Her father had worked hard and diligently, devoting his whole life to his job. Being a registered pharmacist wasn't easy. He diagnosed just about as many ailments as did the town's physicians, and his customers never allowed him to have much time of his own. They needed him. They depended on him. They never knew just when they would be calling on Pavel Skiba next, and it wasn't right, they sometimes said, for their pharmacist to be out of his office in the highly-likely event that some illness might raise up its ugly head and strike them. Her father apparently agreed with them. Pavel Skiba was behind his counter six days a week, and he had never been known to take a vacation or a holiday. But Sundays he set aside for his daughter, and they always left the industrial clutter of Bydgoszcz behind them.

They watched the sails chase the wind, and the wind chase the clouds, and there had never been a dark cloud in the sky.

It was different now.

Christina tossed and turned in the wrinkled folds of her sheet, unable to sleep. The days were bright and cheerful, as crisp as that first hint of frost in the early September air. But nights haunted her, and she dreamed of races with tattered sails and boats that sank. The man with the evil grin beside her was not her father, and he had no name, and she could hear the sound of heavy marching boots drawing nearer. Christina could not escape them no matter how hard she ran.

She crawled from her bed and slipped out into the hallway, startled by the hushed voices of her aunt and uncle. It was not like them to be awake at that time of night, and Christina feared that something was dreadfully wrong. She knelt silently beside the doorway, almost afraid to breathe, worried that they might find her there.

Uncle Arpad sat hovered over his small radio, his head in his hands, trying to make out the words that were squeezed piece meal out of the static.

"It's over," he said, his voice drained of emotion.

"The war?" Aunt Vera caught her breath, and for a moment there was hope embedded in her eyes.

Arpad shook his head, his face paled and his hands trembling. "Poland has just surrendered." His voice was raspy and weak.

Vera turned away. "What will happen to Elizabeth and Pavel?" she asked.

"God only knows."

"When will Hitler stop?"

"When he gets what he wants?"

Vera stood and walked to the window that overlooked the street. Her shoulders were slumped, and her face hung with worry and defeat. "What does he want?" she bit out harshly.

"Everything." Arpad turned off the radio and removed

his glasses. His eyes were tired, but he knew sleep would not come to him that night. "Everything he can get his hands on. That's what he wants. He's a mad man, and there is no stopping him."

Christina's eyes were wide and blurred as she cowered in the darkness. She hid her face and sobbed softly until her aunt found her in the early-morning hours and held her tightly, sitting on the floor beside her, rocking slowly back and forth and whispering, "It's all right, Krischia. There's no need to cry. It'll be all right come morning." But it wouldn't be all right. Vera knew it. And Vera felt as alarmed, as helpless, as vulnerable as her niece.

Poland had surrendered. Her uncle's bitter words kept running through Christina's mind. But what did they mean? She knew nothing about war. She had never heard of this man referred to as Hitler. Was he really mad? Was her homeland lost? Would Poland ever be free again? Where was her mother? And father? Would she ever see them again? Why couldn't she go home? Did she even have a home anymore?

Christina sat in the confusion of those pre-dawn hours, her face pale, her eyes filled with bewilderment. "Why does he want us?" she asked her aunt, her voice barely a whisper.

"Who?"

"Hitler."

Vera shuddered at the mention of his name. "He doesn't," she answered softly, trying to reassure her niece. "There's no reason for him to want us."

"Uncle Arpad said he wanted everything."

A tear unloosed itself from Vera's eyes.

Christina snuggled closer as though trying to hide from the night in her aunt's arms, using them to shield her from the reality of a world she no longer understood. "Will he find us?"

"I hope not, child."

"Will he kill us?"

Vera's sobs were audible now, and her shoulders shook as she held Christina tightly. The darkness was a hollow refuge, and already the faint fingers of daylight had begun to inch their way toward them. She tried to answer the girl, but the words lodged in her throat, and her voice failed her. Vera looked down upon Christina and saw the face of her sister. She uttered a sharp gasp and fainted.

By midmorning, Christina had washed the fatigue from her eyes with cold water, put on her newest dress, brushed the tangles from her curls, and ventured out onto the front porch of her uncle's villa. She sat down on the top step, neatly folding her slender hands in her lap, and looked down the long, crowded street that led past the trees to the far side of Budapest.

She was waiting for the Germans to come.

It wouldn't be long now, Christina told herself. There was nothing left for her to do but sit and wait and wonder what it would be like when the troopers came marching into the city. Would there be fighting? She didn't know. Would people around her die? She forced the thought from her mind. What would happen to her?

Christina's shoulders stiffened.

Hitler wanted everything. At least that's what her uncle had said.

Did he want little children, too?

What would he do with them?

A chill crept over her, and the streets were deathly quiet. In the distance, thunder rattled the sky, or was it the sudden burst of gunfire?

Christina screamed.

She clamped her hands against her ears and screamed again and kept screaming until her aunt dragged her inside and slapped her against the face with a wet towel to silence, then calm her.

"Mama's dead!" she blurted out.

"No, child."

"They came and took mama, and mama's dead." Her breath came in short, painful spasms.

"You're just upset, Krischia," Vera said softly. "There's no need for you to worry your pretty little head anymore. You're safe. Your mama's safe. Your papa wouldn't let anything happen to her. This nightmare will all be over with before you know it, and you'll be home sleeping in your own bed again."

"Promise?"

Aunt Vera kissed Christina lightly on the cheek and hugged her, but she could not soothe the fear that gnawed inside them both.

Poland was home, and Poland had surrendered.

The war was only thirty-five days old.

German armies had stormed across the Polish frontier and pushed frantically toward Warsaw, converging on the capital city from the north, south, and west. The *Luftwaffe* rained bombs down on Warsaw, Gracow, and Lodz, destroying ammunition dumps, bridges, railroads, and entire cities.

Poland's first taste of death had been sudden and swift.

From Warsaw came the report that spread dismay, then panic throughout all of Europe,

> . . . It was the largest army of invasion which had at any-time in history been hurled on the first day of war against an attacked country, 74 German divisions and 2 Slovak divisions.

Stukas screamed in fury from overhead as the warplanes left the stricken land below in flames and in terror. It took less than forty-eight hours for them to devastate the Polish Air Force, blasting most of the planes before they ever had a chance to take off from their airfields. Ground crews were killed or wounded in the bombing run that came from gray, overcast skies.

Heavy guns rolled rapidly down the worn ruts of Polish roads, on through the smoke of wanton destruction that had wasted the countryside.

Only the Polish cavalry rode out to meet the Nazi onslaught, brave and foolhardy, dueling with long lances against the long cannons of the *panzer* divisions. The tanks never slowed down. They kept rolling in a maddened race toward Warsaw, crushing the land but not the spirit of the people who rose up against them.

Thirty-five days.

And it was over.

Christina awoke each morning and listened hard for the sound of warplanes above Budapest. She knew they would come. She was afraid they would be coming for her.

When the German army marched into Budapest, it did so quietly.

There were no bombs. There was no destruction. There was no panic in the streets. No one died.

The German army came as a "friend."

For Christina, war had seemed so far away. Suddenly the grim reminder of war stood just outside her doorway, tall and proud, even haughty, with stern faces and black shiny boots. The guns were silent. But the eyes were deadly. And just down the street, a thin man with a gaunt face quietly moved his office into an empty building. The sight of him made Christina shudder, and she didn't know why. It seemed to her that he was a man without a soul, without even the faint hint of a conscience.

She heard men whisper his name.

"Adolph Eichmann."

It was spoken with fear, never respect.

Late that night, Christina sat playing at a small table in the living room, and she heard her aunt ask, "What will become of us now, Arpad?"

Her uncle shrugged. His voice was calmer than it had been for a long time, and the color was slowly returning to his ashen cheeks.

"The Germans aren't here to cause us any harm," he replied with a sigh. "I wasn't convinced of that at first. But I am now."

"What makes you so sure?"

"The news out of Berlin. The talk on the street." Uncle Arpad neatly folded his newspaper and placed it on the table.

"What do you hear?"

"The governments of Germany and Hungary have made an agreement." Arpad closed his eyes and rubbed them. "We're supporting whatever Hitler does—and Germany is treating us like an ally. Its guns are pointed elsewhere."

"But what about the soldiers on the street?" Aunt Vera's voice was caustic.

"They're here to protect us."

"From whom?"

Arpad shrugged again, his shoulders tired and slumped. "All I know," he said softly, "is that we haven't suffered any. We can sleep at peace at night. None of our friends and neighbors have been killed—"

"What about Poland?" Vera interrupted. Her face was red with anger and frustration.

"There's nothing I can do about Poland," Arpad snapped sharply. "I just want to see my own family come out of this safe and sound."

"And what about my family?" Aunt Vera stood and walked slowly across the floor toward him, her jaws clenched with bitterness. "What about my sisters and my mother trapped in Bydgoszcz? What about little Christina's mother? Are we just going to turn our heads and pretend there's nothing wrong simply because the Germans have chosen to leave us alone while Hitler ransacks the rest of Europe?"

"Hungary had nothing to do with the Polish invasion." Arpad was irritated now. "Count Teleki even told Hitler that on moral grounds Hungary would not take armed action against Poland for any reason."

"That didn't stop Germany."

"Nothing can stop Germany."

"And Hitler has Hungary in his hip pocket."

Arpad closed his eyes and leaned back in his chair. For a moment he was silent, trying to sort out the feelings that churned deep within him, searching for words that might be able to explain to his wife the tenuous position that now confronted the people of their homeland.

"Hungary had no choice," he said at last. "Hitler convinced the prime minister that if Germany is defeated, then Hungary would be automatically smashed, too."

"Do you believe that?"

"No." Arpad sighed. "But I'm only a businessman. I don't make those kind of decisions. I simply go to work each day, try to stay out of the army's way, and pray to God that nothing happens to my family before I come home at night."

Aunt Vera had leaned sadly against the wall, her face as pale as the yellow flowers in the curtain beside her. She glanced at Christina and saw that the girl had stopped playing. She was listening to every word, barely breathing, in limbo, not ever knowing just what tomorrow might bring her, if anything.

There were no secrets.

Not now.

She could shelter Christina, but not from the realities of war that were exploding all around them.

There was no good news anymore. Sometimes, it even seemed to her that the newspaper had the stench of death. And the voice that came through the static of the radio belonged to a man who knew too much, who had seen too much.

Germany wanted everything. That's what Arpad had

said, and he was usually right. He might not like the chaos and turmoil that raged through Europe, but he had accepted it. Vera couldn't, she told herself. Neither could Christina.

Germany wanted everything.

It got Hungary. It got them.

It didn't even have to fire a shot.

Chapter 3

CHRISTINA PAUSED AND LOOKED BACK as the early evening mist began to wind its way around the summit of Gellert's Hill. Soon, that too would be taken from her.

She hurried down the Corso toward the square, already in the shadows of the Greek Orthodox Church, one of its towers lying in ruin beside the classical eighteenth century edifice, the victim of that cold winter day when the sky became black with bombs and the smoke that choked the screams of the dying.

The Danube had turned the color of midnight, and its seven bridges stretched grotesquely from out of the grassy embankment, twisted wreckage where no one walked much, at least not after sundown.

Christina had the street virtually to herself. But she knew that the curious, prying eyes of young soldiers were following her as she ran toward her uncle's villa. Christina glimpsed the stern face of an officer who stood beneath the Romanesque arch of the Belvarosi Templom, the Parish Church of the inner city, a monument to the grandeur of the twelfth century. The soldier looked so out of place, carrying an instrument of death into the ruins of a place where Liszt once played the organ on Sunday mornings and good men knelt to pray for peace.

The music had faded, drowned out by gunfire and the throaty buzz of bombers diving from out of the clouds, the steady clatter of hobnail boots tramping in a deadly rhythm down the Rokoczi ut, the main thoroughfare that led through the city.

And peace? It hadn't come then.

It still hadn't found its way to Budapest.

For so long, Christina thought Hungary would be spared the violence of war. The early days had been the hard ones, filled with anxiety and confusion. She longed for home and closed her eyes each night, carefully remembering each room, each piece of furniture, and she wondered if any of it had changed or if it were still waiting for her exactly as she had left it. Sometimes she could almost hear her father's voice, her mother's laughter. But days became months, and their distant faces were those of strangers.

For awhile, letters came from home. Everyone was fine, Christina would read. Her mama missed her. So did her father, grandmother, and aunts. They all wanted to see her but was glad she was so far removed from the fighting. She sent her love and prayed constantly for the day they would all be back together again.

They made Christina smile.

Then she cried.

After a time, the letters stopped coming at all. Christina kept the last one and read it a thousand times or more, especially when she was happy, especially when she was blue. It was almost as though her mother was talking to her, and she memorized each word. They were too important to ever be forgotten. Christina had opened the piece of paper so often the folds were torn, and the handwriting had become smeared. For so long, she kept it under her pillow at night and never out of her reach. Finally she placed it in the shoe box with her doll and put it away in the closet with her childish things.

Gradually, Christina grew accustomed to seeing German soldiers patrol the streets outside her uncle's villa. They were a nuisance sometimes, but no longer so fearsome. They joked a lot, smoked smuggled cigarettes, and drank all the beer they could find—and they found plenty of it. They weren't mad men, she told herself. They carried guns but never fired them. So many of them were merely boys, barely old enough to shave, easily embarrassed when a pretty girl smiled their way and always hoping that a pretty girl would.

Christina sat on the top step of the porch and watched a soldier with pale blue eyes standing by himself on the street corner, his rifle resting against his leg. She had seen him before, always alone, and she had never heard him laugh. He was different, she thought. Maybe he was simply as lonesome, as homesick as she was.

Christina knelt in her Aunt Vera's garden, picked a handful of flowers that spring had just coaxed from the ground, and ran across the street.

The soldier saw her coming, and his back stiffened. His pale blue eyes narrowed, and he frowned.

She held the flowers up to him. "They're for you," Christina said softly.

He took them from her hand and smiled sadly, awkwardly patting her shoulder. "Danke," he said, and he had a gentle voice. The soldier with pale blue eyes walked crisply away, and Christina wondered why he even carried a rifle. He could never kill anyone. He wasn't like that at all, she told herself. But then she saw him turn the corner, pause, and drop the flowers to the pavement, crushing them beneath the heel of his boot.

Christina heard the neighbor women gossiping about the fighting across Europe, and Uncle Arpad kept close to his radio when he came home at night. But the fear had subsided within her. Her uncle had been right. The German army had no intentions of harming Hungary or its people. The Nazi troops were only there to defend the country.

Then why didn't Arpad trust them?

Why couldn't Aunt Vera forgive them?

Late in the afternoon, Christina glanced out the window and saw her uncle coming home, and he appeared to be more jovial than usual. He took the front steps, two at a time, and walked briskly into the living room, smiling at his niece and beckoning her to him.

She sat beside him and watched while he opened his briefcase, spreading out a handful of official-looking documents before her.

"Christina," he said, taking her hand in his, "it looks as though you will be staying with Vera and me for a long time, at least for the duration of the war. We love you, and I'm glad you're here with me. I know this is not your home, but we'll do our best to make it seem like home. I've had some adoption papers drawn up and signed, making you our little girl."

Christina looked puzzled. "But I'm not your little girl," she said, not quite believing what she had just heard. "I'm mama and papa's little girl."

"I know." Arpad's smile was a patient one. "And you will always be your mama and papa's little girl. But they can't be here. And Vera and I are here, and we'll take care of you, and I promise, Krischia, when the time comes, I'll do what I can to make sure you get back home again."

"But why did you need to adopt me?"

"There are some who might not understand why you are here if you don't belong to us. This piece of paper simply eliminates any problems before they might occur."

Christina looked up, and her eyes met her uncle's gaze, and they never wavered.

"Are you afraid the Germans might take me away from you?" she asked, the color drained from her face.

"Not now." Arpad reached down, wrapped his thick arms around the girl and hugged her. "Nobody can ever take you away now. You belong to us, and, by God, I have the papers to prove it."

"Why don't the Germans like me?"

Arpad sat in silence.

"Is it because I'm Polish?"

"It doesn't make any difference now," he said, standing and brushing the wrinkles from his coat.

"Why do Germans hate Poland?"

Arpad cleared his throat, picked up the papers, and walked toward the hallway. "You wouldn't understand, child," he replied brusquely.

"Why wouldn't I?" she demanded to know.

He paused at the doorway and glanced back over his shoulder. "Because I don't understand it myself," he said, frustration seeping into his voice. "I'm not for sure anybody does."

The ghastly rumors Arpad had heard, he kept to himself. God, he hoped they were only rumors. But he couldn't afford to take any chances. Some were openly saying that the Nazi warlords had a master plan to strip Poland of its countrymen and resettle the land with German citizens. At first, there had only been expulsions. Then had come the mass executions. And finally, Poles were literally being worked to death in labor camps. The Third Reich had simply decided to wipe Poland, as the world knew it, off the face of the earth.

What disturbed him most was the report, written by a high-ranking Nazi official, that had been smuggled out of Berlin. It called for the elimination of every vestige of

Polish culture. It predicted that, in the end, the Poles themselves would be exterminated or die out. It boldly proclaimed that there never again would be a Poland.

Arpad leaned on the door for support. There were some things Christina must not know, and he had taken every step he could in order to protect her.

If the Storm Troopers in Budapest discovered that she had Polish blood running through her veins, the chances were good, virtually certain, that she would be taken out into a deserted field somewhere on the outskirts of the city and shot. It made no difference to them that she was twelve years old. The Third Reich wouldn't be satisfied until the ground had soaked up *all* Polish blood, both young and old. Arpad clutched the papers tightly and walked heavily to his study, carefully locking them away. He prayed that no one would carelessly leak the word that Christina wasn't his daughter, wasn't Hungarian. He hoped the Germans would never ask nor look too closely at the phony documents.

Arpad Bosnyak was a man of wealth, and that brought him a great deal of respect in Budapest. He was looked upon with both envy and grudging admiration as the consummate businessman. Tall and slender, he left for work each day, always dressed in a fashionable suit and tie, the kind of clothes that were befitting to a man about town who owned two beauty shops, a pair of bar-bershops, and, most important of all, a gentleman's bou-tique. Arpad was in his late forties and had medium blond hair, blue eyes, and a neatly-trimmed mustache. To his customers, he was immaculate. The Nazi occupa-tion certainly hadn't hurt his business at all.

There might be a war going on somewhere, but Buda-pest had not suffered, physically or financially. Arpad was making plenty of money, and he needed every cent of it. Vera demanded the best, and she got the best.

Arpad would have it no other way.

Vera was small, stylishly so, barely five feet tall and

never weighing more than a hundred pounds. She, too, was in her late forties, elegant and well educated at the best and usually the most expensive schools Europe had to offer. Vera, the jealous whispered behind her back, was the first lady of Budapest society. At least, they said, she acted that way.

The ballet was her love, and so was the theater. She never missed opening night of any performance, always dressed in the finest clothes that she could find in Paris and Rome. She wore silk, and her gloves and hat became her trademark. Her makeup was perfect. Vera wouldn't leave home until is was. And she had never been seen outside her home with a hair out of place. She wouldn't have stood for it.

The war had shaken her.

But Vera quickly recovered. Society had expected her to do so, and she could not disappoint them. Her smile masked the sadness that bore deep into her soul, but she kept the worry and the pain to herself.

The Bosnyaks had never had any children of their own, and Vera sometimes felt it was a curse to be barren when she had so much to give and no one to share it with. Christina had long been the apple of her eye, her only niece, and Vera did her best to spoil the only daughter of her younger sister.

She loved Christina as her own child.

Now the war brought them together, and Christina's world had been abruptly and inexorably shattered. Vera and Arpad, without complaint, dutifully began picking up the scattered, broken pieces of her life and trying to put them back together again.

Life became as normal as it could possibly be with German patrols strung out alongside the Danube. Still there had been no gunfire to disturb or disrupt the fragile peace of Budapest, and its people tried to forget, or at least ignore, the cries of the dying that echoed throughout Europe and were haunting to the whole world.

Arpad, immaculately dressed, would carefully trim his mustache and shine his cufflinks each morning, then stride off to check his beauty and barbershops before settling in at his boutique. Aunt Vera ruled over the villa with proper etiquette and precision. Everything had its rightful place, and she made sure that everything was where it belonged. A live-in housekeeper kept the villa dusted and reasonably cleaned, but she was never allowed into the kitchen. Vera did the cooking herself.

Slowly Christina accepted her fate. When anyone asked, she freely admitted that she was the only daughter of Arpad and Vera Bosnyak. She called them papa and mama, especially when they were out walking along the Corso and she feared that unseen, unknown German ears might be listening to their conversation.

Arpad, as might be expected of a man with wealth and influence, enrolled Christina in a private girl's school, making sure she received the finest education that Budapest could offer her. Her studies occupied her mind and most of her time, and the memories of home in Poland gradually faded. They didn't keep her awake much anymore. She no longer prayed for the day that she would return to her mother and father. Christina had finally become convinced that prayers, especially those for Poland, were somehow no longer allowed out of Hungary.

On those days when she felt alone, and the pain again surged through her, Christina would run to Gellert's Hill, slowly make her way through the trees to the summit, and watch the setting sun hide its face as the deepening shadows came to swallow Budapest with the night.

The evening star shone down upon her and was reflected far below in the placid waters of the Danube.

Christina knew that it was looking down on Poland, too. And she wondered if anyone in Bydgoszcz had stopped long enough that night to see it, anyone she knew. Was there anyone she knew left in Bydgoszcz?

Christina shivered slightly in the early autumn wind. Why didn't her mother write anymore? She no longer looked for a letter, but always hoped one would come and never let her Aunt Vera know just how disappointed she was, even now, when the postman had nothing for her.

On the night before her seventeenth birthday, Christina sat atop Gellert's Hill and thought about the war that was raging toward the borders of Hungary. For so long, she had escaped its horrors, living quietly in a city untainted and virtually untroubled by the conflict. The Nazi troops had been there to defend them, and the Third Reich was winning, and there had been absolutely no cause for her to worry. Or perhaps she had merely been too young to worry.

Now the news that reached Budapest was sending shock tremors through the city.

The Nazi *Blitzkrieg* had stalled.

The Third Reich was crumbling.

At least those were the rumors. The Allies were boldly sweeping toward Berlin. Adolph Hitler had said all along that Hungary would be smashed if Germany were defeated. Maybe he had been right.

Christina had become more aware of the casualties that littered Europe's battlefields. Millions had died. Millions lay in agony.

At times, she felt so useless. She wasn't a soldier. She would never be permitted to carry a gun and fight. There were just some things that young ladies didn't do. But maybe she could help, Christina thought. Perhaps there was something she could do after all. There atop Gellert's Hill, calm and christened by starlight, Christina made her decision.

"I'm going into medicine," she told her Uncle Arpad the next morning at breakfast.

He arched an eyebrow in surprise. "Do you plan on becoming a doctor?"

"Maybe."

"There's a great need for them." Arpad paused, folded his napkin and pushed himself back from the table. "But it's a long, hard road you're planning to follow." he said. "It's not easy for anyone to become a doctor. And I think you'll find out that it's even tougher for a woman."

"That doesn't concern me."

Arpad smiled. "Nothing ever does," he acknowledged.

"Then you won't try to stop me?"

Now Arpad was laughing. "I'd have just about as much luck trying to stop one of Hitler's tanks," he said.

Christina walked nervously into the college admission's office later that day, collected a handful of forms, and hurried to a table that had been shoved along the back wall. She sat and stared at them for a long time, then sighed, smiled to herself, and slowly began filling them out.

Beside the blank that asked for the degree she would be seeking, Christina wrote in big letters: PRE-MED.

In the distance, the muted sounds of gunfire crept ever closer as Russian troops stormed the Hungarian border, and Budapest braced itself for the onslaught of war.

By Christmas Eve, the city was surrounded. There would be neither a silent night nor a holy one.

Christina stood in the darkened window of the villa and watched her Uncle Arpad and Aunt Vera digging through the frozen earth of the garden, their faces shaded from the moonlight by the low-hanging tree branches overhead. They worked as quickly and as silently as possible, scraping dirt away from the hole and burying a large metal box, filled with Vera's collection of jewelry.

All the Russians want to do is rob you, went the gossip on the street, and it drifted from home to home, as the Red Army, the liberators, drew its military noose tighter around Budapest.

"They're supposed to be our saviors," the old politician down by the square had told Arpad. He spat disgustedly onto the sidewalk and turned his back to the winter wind. "Hell, they're worse than the Germans."

"It'll all be over soon."

"For me, maybe." The politician shoved his hands into the woolen pockets of his coat. "But for the children, it's going to last a long, long time."

Arpad shrugged with weary resignation. "At least the fighting will have stopped," he said. "And Hitler has lost his grip on Europe. We're free of him and his madness. I guess we should be thankful for that."

"The wolf no longer howls at our door," the old politician said bitterly. "But he's been replaced by the bear, and the bear is just as vicious when he's hungry."

"We'll see."

"When the Russians get here, Arpad, don't ever trust them." The politician began walking away as nightfall caught up with him. "I know them. If you open your doors to them, they'll come in and take everything you own. They'll steal with you looking at them and never admit it."

"What do you suggest that we do?"

"Hide every valuable you have where nobody can find it. And if you don't want a Russian to know anything, just look him square in the eye, smile, then lie like hell, and he'll believe everything you tell him is the truth. If you look away or try to hide your face, you won't be able to keep a damn thing from him."

The two men parted when they reached the narrow, snow-covered sidewalks of Rakoczi ut.

Arpad nodded and turned into the wind, but the old man's voice stopped him.

"Remember," he yelled, "the Russians aren't just content to fight the Germans. They want to conquer everyone in the city. They believe that to the victors always go the spoils."

"I won't forget."

"Good luck, Arpad," The old politician forced a smile

and a feeble wave. "We may not see each other again."

Artilleryfire rumbled in the east, and a cloud moved in to blot out the moon. Arpad glanced up into the sky but saw no silver lining. The earth around him, he would tell Vera, was as black as he had ever seen it before.

Christina knelt beside the window and pressed her face against the cold pane, frosted by her breath. Outside, Vera trembled, but not necessarily from the cold.

A gentle snow had begun falling.

The cannons roared again.

They were seldom silent anymore.

Arpad reached down and, with his bare hands, smoothed the dirt atop his earthen vault, then spread broken limbs and decaying leaves across it. He stood and gazed down at his handiwork. No one could tell what he had done. Arpad was sure of it.

He put his arm around Vera's fragile shoulders as she wiped a tear from her eye.

Christina suddenly stood and ran to the closet, frantically rummaging through her belongings until she found the shoe box that held her mother's last letter. She should have buried it, too, Christina told herself.

She knew she would die if the Russians burned it.

Chapter 4

CHRISTINA HAD ALREADY LOST SIGHT of Gellert's Hill by the time she reached the street that wound past her uncle's villa. Dusk was fast losing its grip on Budapest, and the darkness had already begun to wrap its way eerily around the skeletal remains of a downtown business district that had once stood so proud against the fading skylight.

A Russian tank rumbled down ancient streets, and Christina quickened her pace. No one was allowed in the streets after dark, not even a teenage girl who sometimes felt she was being held captive by the same army that had come to liberate her.

An uneasy calm hung over a city that had been bombed, ransacked, looted, and left to the mercy and the judgement of whichever force barricaded itself behind the walls of Budapest. Panic-stricken German soldiers stole what they could carry with them as they fled for their lives. The Russians swarmed in and took what was left.

For weeks, Christina had huddled with her aunt and uncle in the cellar of their home as the Red Army battered its way toward the heart of the city. The shelling was constant from those huge cannons that had been rolled ceremoniously to the outskirts of Budapest. Arpad, in harsh words spoken under his breath, called them Stalin Organs, and the Russian troops clamped down tightly upon the great Nazi war machine whose parts were slowly becoming dismantled and scattered to waste among the ruins.

Guns had roared night and day for almost two full months, and acrid smoke draped across the city like a burial shroud. The Germans had emptied the buildings of Budapest to make room for their weapons and munitions. Rudolph Avenue was virtually blockaded by a hapless pile of broken pianos shoved from the second-story windows of a warehouse that loomed above it. All seven bridges that stretched across the Danube had been mined and blown up, and they lay in charred, twisted wreckage.

Malinovsky had attacked Pest, the primary commercial and governmental section of the twin cities that lined the east bank of the Danube. And Tolbakhim had pushed his troops into the ancient streets of Buda, fighting his way on toward the high western bank that sheltered most of the city's residential area.

Christina expected to die at any moment. The ground trembled beneath her, and the damp chill of winter seeped deep into her bone marrow. Her feet were numb, and her hands hurt, and she shivered beneath the pile of blankets that tried in vain to keep out the cold. The thunder that shook the skies above her was continuous. Her world had no light to warm it. Budapest was blacked out.

By New Year's Day of 1945, the German commander was frantically calling for reinforcements. Berlin ignored him. Two weeks later, he radioed,

IT IS IMPOSSIBLE TO HOLD OUT ANY LONGER.

The Soviet general knew that Budapest was crumbling, ready to fall. He dispatched Russian emissaries, under a flag of truce, to ask for the German surrender.

Nazi sharpshooters gunned them down as they trudged through the snow toward enemy lines.

Tolbakhim cursed and pulled the collar of his coat tighter around his neck. There would be no mercy now, he swore. All of Budapest would pay and pay dearly.

The battle raged at close quarters, and those final, deadly days were fought street by street, block by block, building by building.

Christina, lying in the darkness, suddenly opened her eyes. The shelling had stopped. The gunfire had ceased. The stark silence startled her.

"What's wrong?" she asked, and even her own voice sounded unfamiliar.

"I'm not sure." Arpad struggled to his feet and slipped quietly toward the cellar door. To Christina, he looked so out of place, so unlike himself. His clothes were wrinkled, his hair unkept, and Arpad needed a shave.

He eased the door open and walked outside. He was only gone for a minute.

"Budapest has fallen," Arpad announced softly when he returned. "The streets are full of Russian soldiers, and there's not a German to be seen anywhere, not a live one anyway."

"What shall we do?" Vera asked. The inevitable had come, and still she was not prepared to face it.

"Stay where we are."

"Then what?"

Arpad shook his head and slumped onto a small stool in the corner of the cellar. "I don't know," he said.

Upstairs they could hear heavy boots stomping across the villa's wooden floors. There was a shout, followed by angry voices. The sound of the boots stopped beside the cellar door.

A second later, it was ripped open, and daylight flooded the darkness. Christina's eyes hurt, and she hid them.

"Don't shoot," she heard Arpad yell, "There are no soldiers down here."

"Who are you?" The voice was cold and metallic, void of emotion.

"Arpad Bosynak. My wife and daughter are here with me. That's all."

Christina turned her head and saw the four soldiers crowd the stairwell, their portable machine guns slowly sweeping across the dark hole of the cellar. An officer, his face hardened, motioned for Arpad to follow him up into the villa.

Neither Christina nor Vera moved.

"All of you," he yelled.

Mechanically, they rose to their feet, holding on to each other for support, and stumbled toward the stairs. The soldiers stood back and let them pass. Christina shivered as her bare arm brushed against the cold muzzle of one of the lightweight machine guns. The soldier grabbed her and turned Christina toward him. He had not been that close to a young woman for a long time. He wiped his mouth with the back of his hand and smiled.

"Let her go," the officer snapped.

Christina jerked away and scrambled across the top of the stairs, falling into the villa. The Russian officer stepped across her and walked briskly toward Arpad.

"What do you have for us?" he asked.

Arpad frowned.

The officer prodded him with the barrel of his pistol. "The war has been long," he said wearily. "We are tired of fighting. We are tired of the cold. We are tired of dying. And, most of all, we are tired of Hungary. You, I'm afraid, are the enemy who has caused us so much misery."

"We're not German," Arpad interrupted.

"You are the enemy," the officer screamed. He jabbed his pistol against Arpad's throat, then grinned. "What was once yours now belongs to me. Those are the rules of war."

"We have very little."

The officer spit in Arpad's face. He didn't flinch.

Christina watched as her uncle turned to Vera and said, with resignation, "The pearls, dear. Give him the pearls."

With hesitation, she removed the string of pearls from her neck, barely breathing, clutching them to her chest. "They were a wedding present," she whispered.

The officer jerked them away and the string broke. His soldiers scrambled for the pearls that rolled across the floor. He nodded to Christina. "The bracelet," he snapped.

She handed it to him.

Arpad rummaged around in the bottom of a cabinet, stuffed with clothes, finally pulling out a bottle of wine. He looked at it for a moment, almost lovingly, then bowed slightly, and presented it to the Russian officer. "Perhaps this will take the edge off the cold and help repay you for your efforts," he said caustically.

The officer eyed him with indignation. He ripped the cork from the bottle with his teeth and took a long, slow drink, closing his eyes as the warm fluid washed down his throat. The indignation faded. He passed the bottle on to his men and laughed aloud. "Perhaps it will take the edge off the cold," he mocked. Then his gaze grew intense. "What else do you have for me."

Arpad folded his arms and squared his shoulders as he remembered the words, the final message the old Hungarian politician had given him that day beside the

Rakoczi ut. He looked the officer straight in the eye, smiled, and lied. "That's everything of any value we had left," he said crisply. "The Germans took the rest." He shrugged apologetically. "You know the Germans. They had no regard for anything or anybody."

The officer laughed again as he took the last swallow of wine from the bottle, then pitched the empty container at Arpad's feet.

"The ones who stole from you?" he said indifferently. "Perhaps I killed them for you."

He turned without another word and marched out of the villa, motioning for his men to follow. Arpad glanced at Vera, and she winced noticeably. Christina sat in the floor at their feet. The villa grew deathly quiet. All they could hear was the soldiers' hollow laughter being blown away by the February winds that had come to sting the smoke-blackened face of Budapest.

For the time being, Arpad's plan had worked just as he had hoped it would. The family's valuables still lay untouched and unnoticed beneath the garden's soil. And what they had lost was virtually worthless. He had figured all along that the Russians would be suspicious if he had nothing to give them. So he kept out a string of paste pearls, nothing more than costume jewelry. The bracelet certainly looked silver, but wasn't. And the bottle of wine was not even a vintage year.

Arpad Bosnyak had had the last laugh.

So why did he feel so bad?

Dusk was hovering over the city when the tall, slender Russian major strode without knocking into the villa. He was young, not yet thirty, with high cheek bones and blond hair, impeccably dressed and quite sure of himself. He stood there alone, as straight as a gun barrel, his eyes darting quickly about the room.

He nodded to himself and said matter-of-factly to Arpad, "I'm taking over your villa. It'll work quite well for both my living quarters and my office."

Vera gasped. "What will become of us?" she asked.

"You can't just come in and move my family out into the streets," Arpad argued.

"I have no intention of doing that," the major replied with a quick, almost compassionate smile. "The war has been tough on you, I know. It hasn't been easy on any of us. We'll just get by the best way we know how. The villa is quite large and, I'm afraid, one of the few buildings in Budapest that hasn't been completely demolished or at least shelled quite badly. I believe it can accommodate all of us, as long as you make it a point not to get in my way. How many rooms does it have?"

"Six," Vera answered. "There are three bedrooms, a dining room, library, kitchen, and, of course, two bathrooms."

"Of course."

The major thought for a moment, then told her, "You may have one bedroom, one bathroom, and kitchen privileges. The rest belongs to me."

Arpad opened his mouth to argue, but Vera spoke for him. "Thank you." she said.

The Russian major smiled again. "It's the least I can do," he acknowledged. "I have a family, too. They're back in Moscow." He walked briskly out of the room. "I haven't seen them for a long time." was all he said.

As Christina ran home from her afternoon sojourn atop Gellert's Hill, the shadows of night were chasing along after her footsteps. Behind her, Budapest lay in ruins. More than 30,000 buildings had been destroyed during the Russian siege. Almost 50,000 German soldiers had died upon its bloodied soil. That's what Christina had heard, standing on street corners, listening as old men, aged before their time, fought the war again and again, its miseries embedded deep in their eyes. The Germans had marched into Budapest to defend them.

The Germans had been their ultimate ruination. None of them particularly feared the Russians, but they looked upon them with distaste and distrust.

"Be careful," one had told Arpad. "The major living with you is a member of the Russian secret police."

"He's treated us fairly."

"He's a spy."

Arpad laughed. "Where do you get your information?" he asked.

"It's not hard to come by if you keep your ears open and bribe the right people," the old man told him.

"I'm not afraid of the major."

"His men are."

Arpad shrugged. "They probably have a right to be."

"I'd stay away from him if I could."

"That's hard to do when you're living under the same roof with him."

Christina saw him at the far end of the street, sitting on the front porch of the villa, watching her as she hurried down the sidewalk. He wouldn't approve of her being out so late. He never did.

She sometimes noticed the major staring at her in a strange way that made her blush. It had obviously not escaped him that Christina, at the age of eighteen, had blossomed into full womanhood, always wearing an impetuous smile upon a soft, oval face, as delicate as alabaster and framed by her long, untamed curls.

He treated her like a lady, kind and courteous, but she was always afraid that, deep inside, he might be laughing at her.

The major generally kept to himself. On those occasions when he left the villa, he was driving an American-made jeep. "But it only runs good," the major was careful to explain to her, "if it has a Russian driver."

She giggled.

He was serious.

If one of his jeeps ever broke down, the major simply

walked away and left it sitting in the middle of the street. It was, he admitted one night, easier to confiscate another vehicle than fix the one that had stalled on him. He kicked out the headlights of one jeep that refused to run. He shot another. And one week, the major came bouncing back down the street aboard a fire truck. He glanced up at Christina as she paused beside the porch, and he glowered at her.

"It's almost dark," he said.

She nodded.

"It's not safe to be out by yourself after dark."

Christina laughed. "Are you worried about me?" she asked teasingly.

"Where have you been?" He pulled a small flask out from beneath his jacket.

"To the hill."

"Doing what?"

"Dreaming."

The major grunted and raised the flask to his mouth. He took a quick sip, winced, and said simply, "You're wasting your time."

"Maybe not."

"What were you dreaming about?"

"Going home."

The major raised an eyebrow in surprise. "I thought this was your home."

"Not really." There was a sudden sadness in Christina's voice. "Not anymore."

"You can't escape the war," he said bluntly.

"Someday I will." She looked up into a sky gone black, watching as the clouds rolled together, defying the wind. "There's a rainbow waiting somewhere for me. I know it's out there. And someday I'm gonna find it."

"Those are the foolish dreams of a foolish woman." The major again pressed the flask against his lips, grimacing as he put it back down beside him.

"What are you drinking?" Christina asked, changing

the subject. Her dreams might be foolish, but they were personal and special to her. She certainly didn't want anybody criticizing them, especially a Russian major who might even be a member of the dreaded secret police.

He sighed and stared at the flask. "I can assure you that it's not vodka," he said. "God, it's been so long since I tasted good vodka. And it's not whiskey. I can't even find any bad whiskey."

"Then what is it?"

"All I could find to drink was something out of the truck."

"Gasoline?"

The major shook his head. "Wood grain alcohol."

Christina wrinkled her pert little nose and made a face. "You must be kidding me."

"I wish I were." The major spilled several drops on the top step, struck a match, and dropped it into the fluid. "It's not good," he said. "But it's all I have to drink on a cool, spring night. And it's better than having nothing at all, I guess."

Christina stared in amazement as the fluid blazed brightly until the fire, at last, had consumed it.

"That'll kill you," she admonished him.

"Probably," he answered. His face softened. "Something will someday, anyway."

The major gently cradled the flask in his hands, and Christina slipped inside the villa. He was as lonesome as she was, she thought, and just as lost, just as trapped in a moment of time that neither could escape.

A short time later, Christina heard a jeep, its gears grinding, its engine coughing, pull to a stop just below the bedroom window. Arpad, with his month-old newspaper, and Vera, with her sewing, appeared not to notice. Christina glanced outside.

A tall, long-legged Russian woman, dressed in full military uniform, climbed from the jeep as she did every evening just after sundown. In the moonlight, Christina decided, she was quite pretty, her complexion made even whiter by the straight, raven hair that fell around her shoulders. But she never smiled. She stood at attention as the major pulled himself to his feet, took her by the hand without a word, and led her into the villa and up the stairs to the third-floor bedroom.

Christina heard the door close softly behind them. She wondered if the woman had come out of love or maybe even compassion for the major. Or was she simply following orders like any good Russian soldier would. It bothered Christina for awhile, then she decided that it didn't really matter. For a few hours, for a night, they would have each other to cling to, and neither would have to face the morning alone.

Christina was awakened by the sound of hushed voices. For a moment, she even thought she heard the soft music of a woman's stifled laughter. The door clicked shut, and a jeep, complaining about the cold, roared to a start outside her window. Christina eased out of bed and slipped into the hallway, looking at the old mahogany clock that ticked away the night. It said five o'clock. Daylight was still an hour away.

Breakfast was early, as usual. Arpad and Vera had left for town while Budapest was still deserted, long before the jackhammer sounds of working men, scraping away rubble, rebuilding the bombed-out wreckage of their homes, jarred the city awake. They, too, were working to piece what was left of Arpad's businesses back together. It hadn't been easy. But, slowly, the people of Budapest were coming out of their shell, out of their shock and grasping for a past way of life that would never belong to their generation again. Christina busied herself in the kitchen, washing the dishes, putting them away, opening the window wide to throw the few crumbs that had been left to the birds. A slight noise in the hallway startled her. She turned and saw a young Russian soldier leaning against the doorway, staring at her, casually stroking a two-day growth of whiskers.

Christina's face reddened. She had no idea how long he had been standing there, and his eyes made her shiver with fright. They had the hungry look of a wild animal, and Christina instinctively backed away from him.

"What are you doing here?" she demanded to know.

The soldier grinned, and it was a leer.

"I brought the major some documents."

"You can leave now."

"I'm not ready to go."

The soldier licked his cracked lips, pulled a cigarette from his jacket, and offered it to her.

"I don't smoke." Christina's eyes darted furtively about the room. There was only one way to run if she had to, and the soldier was blocking her way.

He shoved the cigarette into his own mouth and lit it. "You're a damn pretty girl," he said.

Christina held her breath.

"It's been a long time since I had a pretty girl."

Christina felt her knees weaken, and she leaned against the counter top for support.

"Let's go for a walk, me and you," the soldier said, and Christina could almost feel his eyes burn into her skin.

Panic rose up inside of her, then turned to rage. "I'm not going for a walk with you or anybody," she blurted out. Her eyes flashed darkly.

The soldier's grin became a scowl. He leveled his machine gun and walked slowly across the kitchen floor, jamming the muzzle between her breasts.

"I'm not asking you to go for a walk anymore," he said harshly. "I'm ordering you to go, and I'm not waiting any longer."

The barrel of the gun cut into Christina's flesh.

She screamed.

The soldier slapped her. "Shut up," he growled.

She screamed again in pain and agony and anger.

He grabbed her blouse, and Christina could feel it ripping away from her body, and he was laughing, and he smelled of rancid meat and sweat.

Suddenly, he turned loose of her and backed away. Christina fell limply to the floor, and she was vaguely aware of another figure in the room, tall and slender, his dark eyes scowling with resentment. She looked up into the cool, impassive face of the Russian major.

"What's going on here, or do I have to ask?" The major's words were brittle and hard.

The soldier jerked to attention.

Christina nodded weakly toward him. "He's ordered me to go for a walk and threatened me if I didn't go with him." She lowered her eyes and pulled the torn seams of her blouse back together. "Do I have to go?" The rage had drained from her, and Christina's voice trembled slightly.

The major made no response.

He turned abruptly and walked without hesitation into the library, returning as he strapped the leather scabbard that held his pistol around his waist.

He spoke only to the soldier. "Come with me," he said.

"Yes, sir."

Both men marched in step down the hallway and out into the back yard.

Christina rose and watched from the window.

The major, without a word, without a warning, suddenly snapped around, drew out his pistol, and fired pointblank into the young soldier's face, splitting his head wide, then stepping gracefully backward to clear himself of the fall. The soldier, his eyes still wide with disbelief, was a corpse before he hit the ground.

The major stepped over him and strode briskly back into the house, removing the scabbard and gently laying it, along with the pistol, upon the kitchen table.

"He won't bother you anymore." The major's tone was

courteous as always, devoid of emotion. He acted as though he had done nothing more than rid the neighborhood of a stray, rabid dog.

"Thank you." Christina found it hard to look him in the eye. She felt dirty, humiliated in his presence.

"Why?" The major was genuinely surprised.

"He wanted to—" Tears of frustration stung Christina's eyes and stained her pale cheeks. "He wanted to use me, and you wouldn't let him."

The major laughed.

But there was no humor in his laughter.

"What's wrong?" Christina was confused.

"Don't think for one minute that I shot him because of you," the major said, irony piercing his eyes. "He was an official courier. He was on duty. I shot him because he was derelict in carrying out that duty. No more. No less. I expect excellence from my men. I won't tolerate anything else, not from him, not from anyone."

He grabbed his pistol from the table, straightened his shoulders, and walked out of the room. Christina never heard him laugh again.

Chapter 5

THE THOROUGHBREDS CAME AROUND the far turn bunched together, running as one, their feet pounding rhythmically in the soft turf as they dashed madly down the home stretch under the whips of their jockeys. They surged forward, their necks gleaming with lather, and a big black began slowly moving away from the pack, fighting the reins, veering sharply to the inside rail as he stretched for the finish line.

In the Trieste, Italy, clubhouse, Christina was on her feet yelling, her arms in the air, waving triumphantly as the horse bolted past the grandstand, opening up a two-length lead as he swept under the wire.

She suddenly stopped and looked around. Something was dreadfully wrong. Every eye in the place had been turned in her direction, and they obviously did not approve of her.

Christina's was the only voice that could be heard in the quiet, sedate atmosphere of the clubhouse.

She smiled broadly.

The eyes continued to bore through her, and no one smiled back.

Christina shrugged, not particularly concerned, and asked, as naively as possible, "What's the matter? Did all of you lose? The smart money bet on the black."

She smiled again, sat down, ceremoniously crossed her legs, and winked at her uncle. They had come to Trieste on a holiday to visit his relatives, and she had no intention of letting anyone upset her.

Arpad's grin was full of good humor. "Did your horse win?" he asked.

"Of course not." Christina laughed. "I'm not for sure he even finished."

"I thought you must have wagered on the black the way you were yelling for him."

Christina tilted her head in a pixie kind of way and explained softly, "I know I didn't win. You know I didn't win. But everyone else thinks I did."

"Even the Americans?"

Christina glanced over her shoulder at the two young officers, dressed in full uniform, seated at the table just behind her. From the insignias on their caps, she guessed that they probably had something to do with the navy, or least with boats. But she wasn't sure. The tallest one sat with his back rigid, his shoulders squared. He had the well-seasoned, well-disciplined look of a professional who was never really off duty, even when he was. His friend leaned casually on the table, propped upon his elbows, slowly counting the empty glasses that he had collected throughout the afternoon. And the twinkle in his eyes had lost its focus.

"One of them doesn't seem to be having a very good time," Christina said softly. Then she laughed again. "And the other one is having a great time, but I doubt if he'll ever remember it."

Arpad nodded, folded the afternoon's racing program, and laid it in his lap.

"I'm glad to hear you laugh again," he told his niece.

She reached across the table and patted his hand. "I got tired of crying. It only made me unhappy. And when I felt unhappy, I just wanted to cry again."

"The war made a lot of us feel that way."

"Peace hasn't been much better." Christina's voice had a hard, bitter edge. "I'm still a captive. We're all still captives. If you believe that you're free, I'm afraid that you're only fooling yourself."

"The dying has stopped."

"But not the suffering."

Arpad sighed, and a touch of sadness crept into his smile. "Vera and I have done our best for you—"

"You've been wonderful to me," Christina interrupted. "You've watched over me. You've taken care of me. You've been there when I've needed you, and Lord only knows how many times I've needed you." Her face brightened, and she squeezed her uncle's hand affectionately. "You're the only parents I've had for the past seven years, and no one on this green earth of ours has ever had better parents. I love you very much, Uncle Arpad, you and Aunt Vera both. Only God in Heaven can ever figure out how you've been able to put up with me."

Christina giggled.

"You're the daughter we never had," Arpad said solemnly. "And I know that someday we're gonna lose you, and that's hard for an old man to take."

"I may go away for awhile," Christina assured him. "But you'll never lose me. You may try." She laughed again, and this time Arpad laughed with her. "But you'll never be able to do it."

Arpad looked at her and finally accepted what he had known in his heart for a long time. Christina was no longer the little girl who ran after him when he walked to work in the mornings, who sat impatiently on those Saturdays beside the creekbank and waited for him to bait her hook again, who always remembered him in her prayers at night, who had buried her head against his shoulders when the bombs began to fall.

She was a young lady now. No. Arpad had to admit it to himself. Christina, at the age of nineteen, had become a woman, much older and much wiser than her years. War does that to a person sometimes. It shatters some lives. It gives others strength, forging their character like metal in a furnace.

To Arpad, Christina had always been beautiful, even when she ran barefoot through the house with a dirty face and mud on her dress, an angel with the devil in her eyes. Now other men, younger men, were beginning to take an interest in her beauty, too, except, of course, when she was jumping up and down and yelling in the quiet, sedate atmosphere of a racetrack clubhouse. Secretly, Arpad pitied the man, whoever he might be, who chose to marry her.

She quickly scanned her racing program, and the square shouldered American officer glanced her way. He hadn't, in reality, been able to keep his eyes off her, and he had lost more money than usual on the races, concentrating on Christina instead of the horses. There was something about her that fascinated him, and it wasn't really those untamed curls that framed her oval face, falling around her long, slender neck. To him, she seemed so petite, almost fragile, yet there was an unusual, refreshing vitality in her eyes. The officer reasoned that the girl probably wasn't nearly as helpless as she appeared to be. Her olive skin was flawless, and it looked as if it had been burnished and darkened by the sun itself. Her eyes were dark, probably green, he guessed, and she wore an impish smile upon a mischievous face. On her, he decided, it was quite attractive. And her laughter sounded like music, and the officer wondered if she were really as confident, as independent as she seemed to be.

He beckoned to the waitress, ordered another round of whiskey for himself and his partner, and tried to concern himself with the thoroughbreds out on the track, finally giving up, ignoring the results of the last race and never knowing whether or not he was holding the winning ticket.

Arpad was amused by him.

Christina ignored him.

Her uncle leaned across the table, tapped her arm, and said confidentially, "I believe that you have captivated the young American."

Christina glanced up and answered with a hint of nonchalance, "You must be mistaken, Arpad."

"I don't think so." He grinned teasingly. "I should know what interests young men. It wasn't too many years ago that I was a young man myself."

She glanced over her shoulder and, for a fleeting instant, Christina caught the young officer's eye as he stared at her. Embarrassed, he quickly looked away, reached for his racing program, and dropped it.

"You should invite the young man over for a drink," Arpad said with a grin.

"No." Christina's voice was firm.

"Are you afraid?"

"I have no reason to be afraid."

Arpad's eyes twinkled. "For the past several years, you have studied English," he reminded her. "You graduated from college, and I've heard you boast time and again about how fluent you are in the language. You even throw American slang around when you're mad and don't want anybody else to know what you're saying. Now here's your chance to talk to a genuine American— a handsome one, too—and you're afraid you can't do it." Arpad slowly shook his head. "Christina," he said, taunting her. "I'm surprised at you."

Christina tilted her chin defiantly and smiled smugly. "I'm more interested in the races," she answered, turning her attention back to the track as the thoroughbreds neared the starting gates for the fourth race of the afternoon.

Arpad straightened his tie and leaned back across the table. "I'll tell you what," he said, keeping his voice low. "I will bet you money that if you asked those two Americans a question in English, they wouldn't understand a single word you said."

"How much?" Arpad had Christina's attention now. She was proud of her ability to master foreign languages. Her German was almost flawless. She could speak enough Russian to keep herself out of trouble. And she felt quite confident with English, even though all she knew had come straight from a textbook. Besides, Christina never turned her back on a good challenge. She had always been willing to take a risk, especially if there was money involved.

Arpad scratched his chin as if deep in thought.

"How much?" Christina repeated.

Her uncle shrugged. "Twenty-five dollars in Italian *lira*," he answered.

"Okay." Christina was grinning broadly. "What question do you want me to ask them?"

"Just see if they would care to join us at our table for a drink."

Without a moment's hesitation, Christina turned in her chair, brushed the curls away from her eyes, and loudly asked the young officer, "Excuse me, but my uncle wants to know if both of you would like to join us at our table for a drink?"

There was a deadly silence.

The officer squared his shoulders and frowned. His eyes narrowed and confusion registered on his face. He glanced at his partner who simply swallowed the last drop of whiskey in the glass and wiped his mouth.

Christina's heart sank.

Maybe her English wasn't so good after all, she thought. They obviously did not understand her. She had lost the bet, but that didn't particularly bother her. She had also lost face, and Christina felt her cheeks redden, and she was suddenly much too warm for a February day. Her smile slowly withered away.

No one said a word.

No one moved.

Then Christina saw the officer lean forward, cock his head to one side, and clear his throat.

"I beg your pardon," he said with a deep voice, "would you please repeat what you just said?"

"What's the matter," Christina asked shyly, "didn't you understand me?"

A grin bubbled across his partner's face. "Sure he understood you," the happy-go-lucky officer said. "He just can't believe you'd want us to come to your table for any reason, much less for a drink."

"Oh, yes. Please do."

Christina laughed aloud. She was elated. She turned to her uncle and whispered softly, "You can pay me later."

Arpad grinned and nodded.

"I'm John Christy," the quiet, reserved officer said, standing straight and tall beside the table. "And my friend is Ed Jones. It would be our pleasure to join you, if, of course, that's what you really asked us to do."

Christina rolled her eyes and suddenly felt very ill at ease. My goodness, he's formal, she thought, not at all like the Americans she had read about. They had been about half wild and always unpredictable, either blessed or cursed with a devil-may-care attitude and a lust for life that sometimes bordered on the ridiculous. John Christy was obviously different, and Christina didn't quite know whether she liked that about him, or whether she resented it. Ed Jones was about what she expected in an American, standing there with a crooked grin and wrinkles that were pressed into a uniform that he had probably already worn one too many times.

"Ask them to sit down," Arpad snapped at his niece.

His words shattered her thoughts, and Christina smiled awkwardly, quickly pointing to the two empty chairs at her table. "Please sit," she said.

"Thank you."

Ed Jones raised his hand and motioned for a waiter. "I'm not for sure what this was," he slurred, "but I'll certainly have another one."

"You'll have to pardon Ed," John said, forcing a grin that didn't last long. "He's been at sea for the past two weeks, and he takes advantage of very shore leave he gets."

"And you?"

"I make sure he gets back to ship before it sails." John shrugged matter-of-factly. "I depend on him when we're at sea, and, I'm afraid, he depends on me sometimes when we reach port."

"Are you in the American Navy?" Christina wanted to know.

"Merchant Marines."

"And what reason did you have to come to Trieste?"

"We brought a shipload of cattle to Europe," John replied. "We're working with a United Nations Relief Agency to help restore the herds in this part of the world. The war, I understand, took a pretty heavy toll. And there are a lot of people in a lot of countries over here who are going hungry. The agency hopes to rectify that."

Christina crossed her legs and propped her pert chin on the tips of her fingers. "You don't look like a cowboy," she teased.

"I'm not."

Goodness, he's formal, Christina thought. He doesn't even know when I'm joking. He takes everything so seriously. Maybe he's shy. Christina frowned inwardly. Or maybe he just thinks he's better than anyone else because he comes from America. Americans could be arrogant, she had read. She glanced at Ed. Most of them, she remembered hearing, were usually drunk or doing their dead-level best to get that way.

"What do you do on the ship?" she asked to break an embarrassing silence.

"I'm the second officer."

Christina waited for him to explain, but John volunteered no further information.

"I presume that is a job of some importance."

John smiled a shy smile. "It keeps me busy," he said quietly.

"And your friend?"

"Ed is our third officer."

"Then you are his boss."

"We all have our own particular jobs to do."

Christina nodded at Ed, a fresh drink in his hand, a pleased expression on his face. He apparently didn't have a worry in the world.

"Your friend doesn't talk much," Christina said.

"I guess I do the talking," John answered, "and Ed does the drinking. He's much better at it than I am."

Christina laughed. Behind her, the thoroughbreds were running, but for once, she was not concerned. Her interest had shifted from the track to the clubhouse, to the polite young man who sat across from her. Christina had not met anyone quite like him before, and she didn't really know what there was about him that fascinated her so. He was handsome. She would agree with her uncle on that point. And he was very much a gentleman, extremely confident in himself, but not really comfortable with the predicament in which he found himself. Christina was obviously in charge of the conversation, and John no doubt prided himself in his ability to take control of any situation that he might be forced to encounter. Up till then, he had never encountered anyone exactly like Christina and doubted if he ever would again. She was as carefree as a butterfly in flight, so outgoing and refreshing in a land that had known and begat so much bitterness and defeat. Christina settled back in her chair and kept her eyes on John Christy.

She sipped her wine and poured his. This particular afternoon at the Trieste Racetrack belonged to them, she decided. No one else. Uncle Arpad was too busy with his racing form, picking sure winners, but betting on losers. Ed Jones had found all the happiness he wanted or needed in a bottle. He never had figured out exactly what it was, but he no longer cared.

Mostly Christina talked.

Mostly John listened.

It was something they were both good at. And Christina felt a sudden emptiness within her when she realized that the horses were running their last race of the day. It was a feeling she had not expected nor was willing to accept.

The crowd around her was slowly thinning out, but John had made no effort to leave. Arpad glanced at the clock on the wall. Ed Jones, his eyes closed, was cradling one last drink in his hands.

Christina was talking faster now, her English becoming jumbled with Polish words and phrases, not ready for the afternoon to end, afraid she would never see John Christy again and not sure why she would even want to.

Arpad took her hand and pressed a finger against her lips to quiet her.

"Why don't you ask the young Americans to come home with us for dinner tonight?" he asked.

Christina smiled. Arpad had been taking care of her for a long time, she knew. He still was.

She looked back to John and said softly, "My uncle would like for you and your friend to join us tonight at my relatives' house for dinner."

"That's very nice of your uncle." John paused, then asked shyly. "But do you want us to come?"

"Oh, yes." The music had returned to Christina's laughter. "I believe that I would like that very much."

John Christy cut his eyes sharply toward the Third Officer, then said sternly, "I would be delighted to join you, but I'm afraid that Ed must return to duty."

His words jarred Ed's eyes open. "What do you mean," the third officer growled. "I don't have to go back to any ship tonight. I've got as much time off comin' as you do."

"I know that, Ed," John explained softly, "but these are nice people, and you are in no condition to go to anybody's house."

"You think I'm drunk, don't you?" Ed's voice was louder. He tried to stand but slipped back into his chair.

"I know you're drunk."

"I'll be damned if you send me back to the ship."

"That's an order," John snapped.

"You can't do that to me."

"I just did."

Ed glowered at him with angry eyes. "You just want the little woman all to yourself," he bit out harshly. "That's all, and that's a damn poor reason to start pulling rank just because you're afraid that I'll embarrass you."

"That's enough, Ed."

"Yes, sir," he said heatedly.

Arpad took Christina's arm. "What's wrong?" he asked.

"Mister Jones has to decline your invitation," she answered. "Duty calls. He has watch tonight aboard ship, and he's just upset because he would much rather join us for dinner."

"I'm so sorry," Arpad replied. He grabbed Ed's hand, shook it vigorously, and told Christina, "Tell him that we will look forward to his company next time."

"Yes, uncle."

She did, and Ed Jones shrugged as he struggled to his feet, trying for one last swallow from a glass that was already empty.

"Thank you," John whispered to her.

"I regret that your friend got mad at you."

"Don't worry about Ed," John answered. "He's a good man. A night's sleep, and he'll never remember we ever had an argument."

Christina watched the third officer weave his way toward the clubhouse door.

"I hope he finds the ship," she said.

"He's never lost it yet."

She took John's arm, and together they followed Arpad out into the crisp chill of an early February evening. Christina shivered.

"Are you cold?" John asked.

She shook her head. For the moment, there was nothing else to say. They walked in silence, lost in their own thoughts, curious and apprehensive and somewhat unsure of themselves. It was a coincidence that both had been in Trieste at the same time. It was further a coincidence that they had even met each other. A coincidence. That's all it was. Christina didn't believe in them. John Christy did.

Chapter 6

THE SUDDEN JOLT OF THE TRAIN awoke Christina from deep sleep, less troubled than it had been for a long time. She opened her eyes, and the darkness overwhelmed her. Outside, she heard the harsh hissing of steam as the train grumbled and complained and ground to a stop. Through her window, Christina could see the faint outline of a small village nestled against the tracks, quiet and peaceful, with empty streets winding past small, shuttered homes that had been congregated around the sharp iron spire of a country church. Clouds had taken the moon from the sky, and the village had no light at all to interfere with its slumber.

Was she still in Hungary? Or had the train already slipped into Germany during the night? Christina didn't know. Her back was aching, and she shifted her position slightly in the seat, laying her head back against the pillow once more.

The stationmaster yawned and waved to the engineer, and the train lurched forward, clattering through the wooded countryside, carrying Christina home.

She smiled to herself and turned again to the window as the forest flashed past, sinister and foreboding in the darkness.

Home. Christina repeated the word out loud. It had such an unfamiliar, yet pleasant, ring to it.

Home.

Would it look the same? Would it be the same? Seven long years had passed since she last walked through the friendly alleyways of Bydgoszcz, down the street and around the corner to her grandmother's house. She could close her eyes and picture it now, a gray, three-story stone home that had never known a dark or dreary day. At least to Christina it hadn't. The home had been her refuge, and she missed it so. A day hadn't passed without her dreaming of the moment when she would stand tall beside those gardens of roses and cornflowers and see it again.

There would be her grandmother, her Babcha, coming down the walkway, probably with tears in her eyes, her arms opened wide, a broad smile on her face, holding out her hands to welcome Christina back to the city of her childhood, the only place, in reality, where she knew she would ever belong. Her father would be laughing loudly, and she could almost feel her mother's touch, even while the train rolled on steadily through the night.

Home.

Christina smiled to herself and hugged the wrinkled pillow tightly to her chest. For a moment, it seemed so close that she could almost smell the roses and cornflowers, hear the late afternoon whistle that closed down the machine works on the far side of town.

Home.

It was near at last, and Christina knew it, even though she still couldn't believe it. She thought back . . .

The March morning had been unusually warm, even for Budapest, when Christina heard the plodding of heavy boots on the hallway floor. She had just opened the window, and a cool east wind was drying the perspiration from her face. Outside, the flowers were beginning to wilt in the heat, but a thunderhead in the distance promised rain. Soldiers milled aimlessly in the streets, and a dusty haze hung low over the city as construction crews continued to drag away twisted wreckage and debris that still bore the scars of Russian bombs. Christina thought she heard the faint rumble of thunder. Or was it warplanes? She trembled, and her eyes scanned an empty sky.

The plodding of heavy boots stopped outside her doorway.

"Christina." The voice was low, the word slurred—it had the definite Russian accent of their lodger.

Christina quickly brushed aside her curls and turned away from the window. The door slowly swung open, and she saw the major, his unshaven face hidden by the shadows that draped across the hallway. His uniform looked as though it had been slept in, and his thick blond hair was uncombed. A wry grin played at the corners of his mouth.

He entered without an invitation.

Christina breathed uneasily. The Russian major had never violated her privacy before, but his eyes were glazed, and she could smell the bad liquor that stained his jacket.

"What do you want?" she asked timidly.

His grin broadened, and his gaze slowly and methodically surveyed her slender form, silhouetted against the softness of the early morning light. Her olive skin grew flushed, then paled, and she stood there with her legs spread apart beneath the silky folds of her red skirt. Her eyes, he noticed, were frightened, like those of a rabbit caught in a wolf's lair.

The major sighed and seated himself on the edge of her bed, motioning for Christina to come to him.

She shook her head.

The smile shriveled away, and the major straightened his shoulders. He looked down for a moment at the papers in his hands, then pitched them abruptly upon the bed.

"These will get you home," he said sharply.

A look of bewilderment crept into Christina's eyes. She said nothing.

"You do want to go home, don't you?" The major's voice was tinged with irritation.

"Yes."

"Then go."

The major stood, and Christina saw the weariness embedded deep in the lines on his face. It was obvious that his nerves were on edge, and he would probably settle them down again with cheap whiskey as soon as he left the room. At first, the major drank only at night, or only when, he said, he was officially off duty. But, lately, Christina realized that she never saw him completely sober, day or night.

She walked apprehensively to her bed and gingerly picked up the papers, staring at them in disbelief.

"They are in order, I assure you," the major said. Fatigue had replaced the irritation. "These documents will allow you to travel to Vienna, then on to Berlin. You can report to the Russian headquarters in Berlin and pick up the necessary papers that permit you to re-enter Poland."

Christina felt weak, and, for a second or two, she was afraid she would fall. She reached out and braced herself against the major's arm, suddenly realizing that she couldn't read the papers for the tears that had blurred her eyes.

"Thank you," she whispered. Christina tightly clutched the papers to her bosom and looked up at the major. "Why are you doing this for me?"

He shrugged and stepped away from her. "Everybody needs to go home sometime."

"And you?"

"Someday."

"I'll never forget you."

"Yes, you will." His smile was a sad one. "There is nothing to remember. We were here, you and I, and neither of us ever wanted to be here. Tomorrow will be different." The major walked briskly to the doorway, then paused, and looked back at Christina. His grin only lasted an instant, then it was gone. "Tomorrows are always different, thank God."

"Do you believe in God?"

"I'm alive," he said sharply. "I must believe in something, and I have to blame someone for sending me to Budapest to die."

The major stumbled out of the room, and the shuffling sound of his boots echoed down the hallway.

Christina heard the front door slam.

The sharp crack of thunder was closer this time.

"Thank you," she whispered again.

But no one heard.

Christina had packed her bags before the week was out. She hugged her Uncle Arpad and kissed her Aunt Vera and felt a twinge of regret for leaving them. They had, in reality, been her parents when she had none. They had supported her and loved her and sent her to the finest school in Hungary. They had sheltered her and comforted her when the bombs fell around them. They had cried with her when the letters from Poland stopped coming. And they had let Christina grow to womanhood, strong and proud and independent. For seven long years, Arpad and Vera had been all that she had, and she knew she could not have asked for anything more or anything better.

Christina had left shortly after dark, keeping the tears inside of her, watching as Vera dabbed her eyes and tried to smile even when she couldn't.

"Do you have enough money?" Arpad wanted to know.

"Yes."

"Are you afraid?"

"A little."

"Kiss your mother for me."

"I will."

"And tell your father that he and his comrades fought a brave fight. We're all proud of him."

Christina had nodded.

"And take care of yourself."

"I'll be fine." Her voice had been unsteady. "Don't worry about me."

"Write us," Vera had called.

The taxi horn had honked before Christina answered. She turned to run down the sidewalk, pausing beside the street to look back over her shoulder. Arpad was standing there, his arm around Vera. They were waving, and Christina suddenly had the feeling that she might never see them again.

"I love you," she yelled. "I love you both."

The wind whipped her words away, and she hoped they had heard. She hoped they knew. She wanted to run back to the villa and hug them again, but the taxi was pulling away from the curb, carrying her into the night, carrying her toward Poland and home.

Christina couldn't take her eyes off the villa as it slid back into the darkness. An upstairs light was on, and she thought she caught a glimpse of the Russian major looking down at her as the taxi rounded the corner. A feeling of remorse gripped her. She had been in such a hurry. Time had slipped past so quickly. She was gone, and she hadn't even told him goodbye.

The major, she knew, had been right.

Christina had told him, "I'll never forget you."

"Yes, you will," he had said.

And she had.

Christina opened her eyes and stretched to ease the tension in her muscles. She shifted her weight and saw the reflection of her face in the smudged window of the train. It looked much older than her nineteen years, she thought. She wondered if her mother and father would even recognize her anymore. They had left behind an impetuous twelve-year-old in Budapest. A woman was coming home. In her mind, she could not imagine how or if the years had changed them any. Her father's hair would probably have a little more gray in it, and her mother no doubt would be a few pounds heavier. Well, she would know them, no matter how badly the hunger and punishment of war had scarred them.

Christina tried to sleep, but it was useless. The dream she had dared not dream was coming true.

She laid her head against the back of the brown, stained seat and watched the countryside rush past in the darkness.

Christina had changed trains in Vienna with no trouble, and that, she decided, was definitely a good omen. Her documents had been quickly checked and approved by a sleepy official who didn't really care who she was or where she was going. Christina had simply been one among thousands, all lost, all part of the faceless mass of humanity that had become scattered or misplaced throughout Europe. The names weren't important to him, and the sleepy-eyed official, probably working at a job that he didn't like or want anyway, certainly hadn't pitied any of them. They were nothing more than a nuisance, and he was only interested in getting them out of his way for the night. Let someone else worry about the homeless. Let someone else take responsibility for them. He felt better each time a train pulled out, loaded with people he didn't know and, with any luck at all, would never have to see again.

Christina glanced around her. A woman with a worn face, wearing a dress much too large for her, suckled a baby in the darkness. A Jewish man, his jaws sunken, his eyes tired, leaned heavily on a cane. Christina couldn't help but notice that the glass in one side of his wire frames was missing. The baby had cried until the train slipped beyond the lights of Vienna. The woman had sung, soft and low, too mournful, Christina thought, for a lullaby. The Jewish man had not spoken at all. He stared at the floor, his lips moving, and Christina wondered if there was anyone but God left to hear his prayers, if he, indeed, were praying.

The rhythmic clatter of the wheels hugging the track carried her on toward Berlin.

Then to Poland.

Home.

The sound of drunken laughter jolted Christina out of her half-dream, and she sat up with a start. She could not understand the words. They were too far away. But the accent sounded so familiar.

It was definitely American.

Christina relaxed and smiled to herself. American servicemen were a funny breed, she thought. They talked too loudly and drank too much and loved to fight with anyone, especially with each other. Perhaps they were homesick—maybe homesickness did that to them. They were rowdy and carefree, too, and usually believed most of their own lies, even when they were making them up. Christina had watched the American soldiers crowd onto the train at Vienna. They were young, so young, but the war had aged them, and European women she heard, had educated them. They had offered her food.

"I'm not hungry, thank you."

And cigarettes.

"I don't smoke."

And bad whiskey.

"Keep it for yourself."

All they had wanted, she decided, was a woman for the night, if only someone to talk to. They had not had it easy. War had been horrible for them, too. But they were tough. At least they tried to act that way. But more and more, Christina saw that they were simply lonely and a long way from home.

She understood.

For a time she laughed with them and heard the songs they sang and listened while they talked about the girls they had left behind. When one bottle was emptied, somebody, it seemed, always had access to another one, and the laughter would begin again. They bragged of their victory in Europe as easily as did of their mother's fried chicken. They had seen death. They had dealt it. They had been able to outrun it. They were the survivors, and at times they wondered why.

Some bet on their cards, some on the roll of their dice. Money was of no real use to any of them. They won a little and lost a little and gave a little away. They used the whiskey, both good and bad, both bought and stolen, to wash away the bad memories of yesterday. They could sleep off today in a drunken stupor. Few worried about tomorrow, although almost all of them, Christina knew, feared it.

So did she.

The American soldiers had grown more raucous as the night wore on.

For awhile, they had captivated Christina. They had fascinated her.

They reminded her of John Christy.

The soldiers on the train were what Christina had always thought those high-spirited Americans would all be: probably half wild and unpredictable, either blessed or cursed with a devil-may-care attitude and a healthy lust for life that sometimes bordered on the ridiculous.

John Christy, however, was different.

She pictured him again in her mind, straight and tall, quiet and reserved, probably too disciplined and much too formal. He didn't smile often, but it was a warm smile when he did. Christina had never quite figured out whether John Christy was arrogant or merely shy. Now she would never know, and in a way that saddened her.

He had been a gentleman and a gentle man in a world torn apart by the savage barbarism of war. Yet, he was also an enigma, and Christina was certain that she had never met anyone quite like him before.

For three evenings, John Christy had been at her side as they walked the lonely streets of Trieste together. He escorted to her to the finest restaurants, toasted her as they sat surrounded by music in open-air courtyards, their faces aglow in the dim lights of the lanterns that reached out to brush the shadows away. He held her close as they danced far past the midnight hour, oblivious to those around them, lost in a moment that neither understood but would never forget.

At first, John Christy had merely been a curiosity, an American stranded in a foreign port. He was alone, and so was she. He had no one to occupy his evenings, and Christina was bored. Together, they might be able to help each other find a few, fragmented hours of happiness. There hadn't been many of those for either of them in a long time. Their paths had crossed, by chance, and soon they would part, and, within a week or two at sea, John would have forgotten her name. Christina was sure of it. And when she slept at night, he never even crossed her mind.

"Tell me about your American friend," Aunt Vera had said at breakfast the morning after John had joined them all for dinner.

Christina yawned and wiped the sleep from her eyes. "He's nice," was all she said.

Aunt Vera smiled. "He's also quite good-looking."

Christina shrugged and ran her hand through her unruly hair. "I think he knows it, too," she replied.

"Well, I'm sure the fact wasn't lost on you."

Christina broke down and laughed. "I think John's a

little too perfect," she said. "He likes ballet. He loves the opera. In fact, we're planning to go see *La Boheme* tonight. He always orders the right wine, knows the right words to say, and he dances like a dream."

"John sounds like a real man of the world. But then, I'm sure he's seen a lot of it."

"The sea makes sure of that."

"In a way that's sad." Vera poured herself another glass of milk from the antique pitcher. "John spends so much time at sea that he no longer has a home he can really call his own."

"Perhaps not. Anyway, don't feel sorry for John. He may not have a home, but I'll bet he has a girl waiting for him every time his ship pulls into a port."

Vera arched an eyebrow in surprise. "What's the matter, Krischia?" she teased. "Are you jealous?"

"No." Her tone became serious, and she stood and walked toward the breakfast room window. Outside, the clouds had darkened the sky, and there was a threat of rain in them. Christina folded her arms and stared at them in silence for a moment, then continued, "Then again, maybe I am jealous of John. I don't care how many women he has waiting for him in how many ports. That's his life. That's his business. But I am jealous of his freedom. John can go anywhere in the world he wants. I can't." She sighed deeply.

"And where would you go if you had the chance?"

"Home."

Vera looked away and busily began buttering her dried toast. "Is that all you ever think of?" she asked, a slight tremor in her voice.

"Yes."

"Someday, you'll get there, Krischia," Vera replied softly.

"Someday may be too late."

Christina abruptly walked away from the window and went to her room. She locked the door behind her and stared with disgust at the thin, sad-eyed face looking back at her in the mirror. Sometimes she thought she was beautiful. But on this particular morning, all Christina could see was the plain face of a homely girl, maybe not ugly, but certainly not beautiful.

And she wondered why John even wanted to see her again. There were plenty of girls in Trieste to interest him, older girls, wiser girls, girls who would have gladly invited him home to share their love and their bed with him for the night, probably for free.

Christina didn't even offer him a kiss, and she felt a little guilty because she hadn't.

Maybe she simply resented the fact that John was so sure of himself.

Maybe it was because she wasn't very sure of herself anymore. Christina put on a brave front. She could act as cocky as anyone, even John Christy. Down deep inside, she felt more like a little girl trying hard to be a woman and not doing a very good job of it. Reality had become so difficult to face, and she had lost faith in her dreams.

John had promised to pick her up at seven, and still she wondered why. To her, it just didn't make any sense.

He was a man. She was a mere child. Or was she?

Christina grinned. Maybe not, she thought. Maybe she was a woman after all, just learning to be a woman. Maybe John could teach her. She lay back on her bed, closed her eyes and waited for him to come to her.

Chapter 7

CHRISTINA NO LONGER HEARD THE MUSIC. She watched as John gingerly filled her glass again with wine and knew that she was probably drinking too much. At the moment, she didn't care.

"Would you like to dance?" John asked softly.

"No." Christina leaned back in her chair and shifted her gaze to the night itself. For an instant, the moon broke through the clouds, then it was gone again, and the darkness crept back in around her. She shivered in the February chill and felt John suddenly take her hand in his. Christina smiled. The time for dancing had passed them by. She sipped on the wine and wondered what thoughts were going through John's mind.

It wasn't like him to be so quiet.

For the past three nights, Christina had learned a great deal about this Merchant Marine officer from America who had gone out of his way to court her. He had talked easily about himself without any traces of embarrassment, although he kept assuring her that his past wasn't particularly interesting and could probably be classified as boring.

"I'll be the judge of that," she replied with a laugh.

John Christy had been born twenty-one years earlier in Portland, Maine, the oldest of seven children, the son of a solid New England family. When he was fourteen, his mother and father had been divorced, and to him it was a sad, sordid blemish that he could never forgive nor forget. John blamed his mother, yet he remained the apple of her eye, the eldest, the talented, the shepherd of the family. In her sight, he could do no wrong. In his sight, she had foolishly broken apart everything that was important to him, including his heart. He wasn't comfortable with women who were domineering, who reminded him of his mother. He had rather be alone. John Christy spent much of his time alone.

The sea had become his refuge.

For days he had sat on the front porch of his home and waited for his father to come back.

"You're wasting your time," his mother had yelled.

"Why?"

"He's not coming back."

"Why?"

"I won't let him."

One day, John realized that his mother was right. The roadway that led in front of their little New England cottage only led away from home. No one who took it ever came back down it again.

John would have cried. Except that men don't cry, he told himself.

He would have followed his father.

But he had no idea where his father had gone. His mother knew, but she wouldn't tell him.

He felt a burning rage tear through his innards. John didn't understand. It would be years before he did, before he finally learned that the courts had given his father instructions that caused a grown man to cry. He was to leave. He was to keep going. He would never be allowed to see his children again.

John sat and waited for him anyway.

A year later, he shrugged his shoulders in despair, gave up hope, and left home, too, enrolling in the Maine Maritime Academy.

He was there, studying late into the night, when he got the unexpected telephone call from his mother.

"John, I just wanted you to know that I've gotten married again," she said.

Silence.

"He's a good man, John, and I'm happier than I've ever been in my whole life."

Silence.

"He's going to be good for the children, too. He has agreed to go down and officially adopt all of you."

"I don't want to be adopted," John said sharply. "You can change your name. That's your business, mother. I'm keeping the name I was born with, and I'll die with the name I was born with."

"I do wish you would change your mind, John." His mother sounded perplexed.

Silence.

"John, are you still there?"

He gently hung up the phone, picked up his history book, and threw it against the wall. It was the last time that John Christy allowed himself to show the festering anger that boiled down deep within him. That, he thought, was a sign of weakness. John Christy had no use and little respect for those who did not possess the inner strength, the discipline to face life on its own terms, both the good and the bad and the inequity of it all.

Two weeks before his eighteenth birthday, John became the youngest officer to ever graduate from the academy. His mother was there, standing proudly by his side, and so were his brothers and sisters, as well as the new man who shared his mother's house and had so gloriously agreed to adopt him.

John, standing straight and tall, smiled at them all, and no one saw the pain and anguish that were branded deep in his eyes. John Christy made sure of it. To his family, he was without fault. They simply refused to believe that he had hurts or flaws, and John found it easier to keep them to himself. None of them ever saw behind the steel facade of his smile.

"You'll be coming home now, won't you John?" his mother had asked.

"No, ma'am."

"It would be good to have you there," the new man in his mother's life assured him.

"Thank you, but I have other plans."

The sea was calling him. There would be a ship sailing soon from some port, and John Christy was determined to be aboard it. His dreams, his ambition lingered far beyond the boundaries of Maine. He was his own man, even at the age of seventeen. He would be his own master. And John would find solace, a place of his own, within the restless waves of the sea.

It would take him to places he had never seen before, to some ports he had never heard of before. Finally, four years later, it had brought him to Italy and to the side of a carefree, saucy little Polish girl who had captivated his mind, if not his heart.

John's smile was a sad one, and he had not spoken for several minutes. He held Christina's hands tightly as candlelight danced impetuously across their faces.

"There's something wrong—isn't there John," Christina said, breaking the stilted silence. The lilt was gone from her voice.

John didn't answer. His gaze became intense, boring into her, and Christina could almost feel the penetrating heat of his eyes. He reached up and touched her face, gently and softly, with his fingertips, and she was surprised at how cool they were. The flame on the candle between them bent with the wind, and a shadow took the last traces of John's smile away. For a moment, all Christina could see was his eyes, and they held her tightly as his hands.

"What's wrong, John?" Her voice was almost a whisper.

"All my life I've looked for someone like you, and until now I never believed that someone like you really existed."

Christina started to laugh, then stopped when she saw the grave look on John's face.

"And now that I've found you, I have to lose you." John shrugged and forced a grin. "That doesn't seem fair, does it Christina?"

"I'm not for sure I know what you're talking about."

"The last three days have been the best three days I've ever spent," John told her.

Christina patted his hand. "I've enjoyed them, too," she replied. "I had almost forgotten what it was like to laugh again. And when we danced, the war seemed so far away. As if, maybe, it had never happened." Christina giggled. "Besides," she teased, "I've been able to practice my English on a genuine, authentic American."

"I don't want to leave you, Christina." John's mood was somber. "But I've received word this afternoon that we sail early tomorrow morning."

"But John, you knew you would only be in port a few days when you got here."

He nodded. "For the last three days I've known it. I just didn't want to believe it. Now I'll be leaving you, and Christina, I do believe that's the most difficult thing I've ever done in my life."

Christina frowned. "You're serious, aren't you?"

"I've never been more serious."

"John, we hardly know each other. You're a dashing young Merchant Marine officer. I'm just a frivolous little Polish girl on holiday. We met simply because my uncle bet me twenty-five dollars that neither you nor your friend would be able to understand my poor, broken English. We've shared three evenings together. They have been very special times for me, and I'll be leaving with memories I know that I can never forget. For those, John, I'm thankful, more than you will ever know. I've always been a little girl trying to grow up. You've made me feel like a woman. For me that's a very unfamiliar feeling.

"But, John, we both knew the day would soon come when your ship would be sailing. You'll return to the sea, and I'll go home to Hungary. You will no doubt find another girl in another port somewhere; I will try to find a way back to my family in Poland. The barriers of war can't last forever."

John Christy straightened his shoulders and refilled their glasses with wine. He raised his in a toast to her. "To the most beautiful girl I've ever met," he said softly.

Christina blushed.

She started to protest, but his eyes stopped her.

"Within a few months, my ship will be coming back with a new load of supplies," he continued. "Can I see you then?"

"I don't really know where I'll be."

"I have your address in Budapest."

"I may be in Poland."

"I'll find you."

"John, you had me fooled." Christina laughed. "You're a crazy American just like the rest of them."

"Maybe," he shrugged, "but it's important for me to see you again."

"Unless you forget me." Christina's mock pout burst into a broad grin.

"There are some things I'll never be able to do," John answered. "And that's one of them."

"We'll see."

John nodded and emptied his glass. He took Christina's arm and together they walked out into the chilled February night. It was late, and the streets were virtually deserted. Even the taxi driver was yawning. Christina glanced up at the big clock on edge of the square. It said two-thirty, and reality gripped her. John would indeed be leaving tomorrow—and tomorrow had already come.

He kissed her lightly on the lips as he said goodbye, then stepped back off the porch and watched until Christina had walked through the doorway of the home where she, Arpad, and Vera were staying. He saw her wave, an awkward, timid wave, and the door clicked shut. John stood there in the darkness, remembering each delicate feature of her face, every graceful movement of her body. He knew chances were good that he would never see Christina Skiba again, and he burned the image of her memory deep into his mind. To him, she would never age. She would forever be nineteen, and he would be able to see Christina anytime and everytime he closed his eyes and thought of her.

The morning was gray and overcast, and the trees outside Christina's bedroom window were wet with rain when the sudden knock on her door awakened her. She lay there for a moment, rubbing her eyes, trying to talk her tired and aching body into moving. It must be the wine, she thought. God, how much wine did she and John consume? The vineyards of Italy should seriously consider sending them a thank you note. It was funny, though. Last night, the wine hadn't affected her at all. She was in control of herself and in command of all her senses. It had waited until she went to sleep to ambush her, and it must have hit her pretty hard. Her head was swollen, her legs weak, and there was an uneasy feeling throbbing in the pit of her stomach. Christina groaned. She heard the knock again, louder this time.

"I'm coming," she yelled, then grimaced at the harsh sound of her own voice.

Christina rolled out of the bed, threw her robe around her shoulders, and opened the door.

Aunt Vera was standing there, holding a bouquet of red roses. She handed them to Christina. "They're from your American friend," she said. "He must think you're a very special girl."

"He's crazy."

"I think he's crazy about you."

"He's gone." Christina yawned. "His ship sailed this morning. He's already on his way home."

"I'm sorry." There was genuine sympathy in Vera's voice.

"That's all right," Christina answered. "He was very much a gentleman, and we shared some good times together. But John has his life to live. And I have mine. He's going in one direction, and I'll be going in another. He said he didn't want to leave me, but you know how men are when the wine has gone to their head."

"And when they're holding a pretty girl's hand."

Christina laughed.

"It was a beautiful night," she said. "Everything was perfect. I think that Second Officer John Christy just let himself get caught up with the magic of the moment." She shrugged. "He even promised to write me. Men, from what I've been told, have a tendency to be full of empty promises. We'll just have to wait and see."

Vera held an envelope out to her.

"What's that?" Christina asked.

"It's a letter." There was amusement in Vera's eyes. "It's from John."

Christina took it and sat down on the edge of the bed, laying the roses across her lap. For a long time, she stared at the letter without opening it. What on earth had John written her his last morning in Trieste? Perhaps, he was telling Christina that he loved her. She didn't want to hear that. Perhaps, he was admitting that she was right, that their paths probably never would cross again, that they no doubt would never see each other again. Christina didn't want to hear that either.

She glanced out her bedroom window, and in the east, where the clouds had broken, she glimpsed the faint, pastel hues of a rainbow bending across the sky. Was it forming? Or was it fading? Christina didn't know. At the moment, the rainbow was as elusive, as hard to grasp and understand as her own emotions.

The train rushed on through the night, and gradually even the drunken laughter of the Americans died away. The baby slept, cradled in the weary arms of its mother. The elderly Jewish man had slumped against the window, his mouth gaped open as if in death. Only an occasional snore assured Christina that he was still alive. She stretched and shifted her weight in the seat, restless, unable to find any position that was comfortable. The night had been in no hurry to pass. Sleep had definitely decided not to waste any of its time on Christina. She dreamed with her eyes open.

Of home.

That didn't surprise her.

Of John.

That did.

She reached in her purse and removed his letter again. It was wrinkled by now, stained and torn. The darkness of the night made it virtually impossible for Christina to read it again, but that didn't matter. She already knew each word by heart.

The letter was formal, written as though the young officer was simply writing out a morning report for the ship's captain. Christina had expected as much from

John Christy. He was organized. He was disciplined. He kept his emotions to himself. Only once had Christina seen the facade crack: that last night in Trieste when John, for a few minutes, let down his guard long enough to tell her how badly he hated to leave her. For an instant, she thought, she had glimpsed the real John Christy. She would have liked to know more about the man hidden away behind the strict, rigid restraints of his military training. Christina knew she never would. There had been a kindness in his eyes, compassion in his voice. He someday would give himself to someone else, and Christina felt a sharp pang of jealousy. That angered her. She believed in having dreams, but not in lying to herself. He had written:

Dear Christina,

You are the first girl from Poland I have ever met, and I have never known anyone exactly like you. Perhaps there is no one else who could have captivated me so completely with her charm and wit. You understand life and know how to fully live it, and I envy you for that.

At the racetrack, I sincerely appreciate how you helped me protect my drunken friend from any serious embarrassment on his part. When he sobered up, he was quite repentant for his actions and asked that I express his gratitude to you as well. You came to our rescue in an awkward moment and proved to me just how smart and observant you really are.

Christina, regardless of what you said, I shall never be able to forget you, and I won't rest until I have the opportunity to see you again anywhere you might be.

Fate drew us together. And, somehow, I believe that fate will find a way to bring us together again.

By the time you receive this letter, an ocean will be separating us. But my thoughts are with you. They will always be with you.

Christina sighed and wondered if John were thinking of her as the train raced on toward the dawn and Berlin.

She doubted it. John was simply a hopeless romantic beneath that arrogant exterior of his. He probably fell in and out of love as easily and as often as the sun rose and set.

There was no reason for her to even keep his letter. Yet the envelope was filled with dried rose petals. She couldn't bear to throw them away either. Christina laughed softly to herself. Maybe she shouldn't blame John. Maybe she was the hopeless romantic who, down deep, kept lying to herself after all. Well, she thought, lying was all right sometimes if she wasn't foolish enough to believe it. The train entered Berlin from the West, and, through her window, in the pale light of early morning, Christina saw a city in ruins. The sight stunned her, sickened her. The bombs had destroyed Berlin, and the charred, tangled remains of burned-out buildings rose up against a gray sky like the arms of lifeless skeletons that had reached out too late for help that never came. The Third Reich had defended the city until there was nothing left to defend. Their concrete anti-aircraft shelters had saved their lives, but not their hopes. Their strength had come from the grand delusions of a mad man, but now the strength and the delusions both had been swept off the tattered, blood-stained face of Germany.

The train steamed to a stop, and Christina followed the mother and child into the crowd that was wearily pushing its way toward the station's platform. The aging Jew, his eyes haunted by the ruins that stretched endlessly before him, hadn't moved. His hands were clasped beneath his chin, and up ahead, the baby began to cry again. Christina looked slowly from one to the other. It was the beginning of life and the ending of life, both on their way to a home that had been and now truly no longer existed for either of them.

A tear ran slowly down the old man's face, and Christina turned away from him. He would grieve alone but not aloud. Poor all of us, she thought. How many tears are left?

"It's all gone," Christina heard him whisper.

The aisleways were packed and stuffy, and they smelled of sweat and stale beer. An elbow jabbed into Christina's ribs, and the air was stagnant and suffocating. There were so many people in a hurry, pressing their way forward, waiting, then cursing for the doorways to open. She was caught in the midst of a suppressed bedlam that was about to explode. Christina felt the sudden rush of a cold wind against her face, and the crowd of people bolted one by one out of the train, carrying Christina with them. She stumbled forward, found herself out on the wooden platform, and looked around, frowning. She had no idea where she was, but that no longer mattered.

She had reached Berlin.

She was one step closer to home than she had been in a long time.

Her eyes turned eagerly toward the Polish border, lying somewhere beyond those cracked, broken concrete walls that had once echoed with the tumult and the chaos of the madman's call for power. His voice had rattled them. The bombs had shattered them.

Now Berlin shivered in the funereal quiet of a frosty March morning.

Christina pulled her brown Persian lamb jacket tighter around her shoulders, picked up her suitcase, and waved for a taxi circling the railroad station.

"Where to?" the driver growled.

"To the Russian commandant's headquarters." Christina spoke crisply and without emotion. At the moment, she was simply too tired to be nervous or exuberant.

The driver eyed her suspiciously. Christina was obviously in a city where she did not belong. Her clothes were much too nice, much too fashionable. All around her women with hollow eyes and sunken faces were laboring all day long in the streets of Berlin, clearing away rubble from the ruins, piling it into heaps of broken stone and twisted metal. Their dresses were patched and torn, old and wrinkled. They wore rags around their feet. Shoes, even when the chill of winter gripped the countryside, were a luxury that few of them could afford. Many women simply wore boots that had been stolen off the feet of dead and dying soldiers, boots that were much too big for them.

"That's a rough part of the city," the driver said as Christina slid across the back seat of his taxi. "It's no place for a lady to be alone, I can assure you."

"I'm expected."

The driver arched an eyebrow as though his suspicions had been confirmed. Nobody could trust the Russians. They had too many spies in too many places. Some of them, he told himself, were good-looking dames.

He pulled his woolen cap down over his ears, blew on his cold hands to warm them, and drove on toward the eastern sector of Berlin in silence.

Christina hoped that someone would be expecting her at the Russian commandant's headquarters. She opened her purse and again pulled out the documents that had allowed her to travel this close to home. She read them again and smiled, remembering the words of the major who had shared their villa in Budapest.

"In Berlin," he had said, "the Russian commander will provide you a visa to Poland."

"What if he refuses?"

A cynical grin had played across his face. "You will have no trouble," he assured her. "I am writing him for you. We spent the long, cold seige of Leningrad together. He will remember. And you will have no trouble. I promise you."

The taxi braked to a sudden stop before a bleak, gray stone building that, to Christina, seemed to blend quite well with the stark, winter monotony of the Berlin landscape. She got out, paid her fare without a word, and raced up the steps to the front door.

Inside, the building was as bare, as nondescript as its exterior. Guards, standing at attention, hungrily ran their eyes up and down Christina's lithesome body as she walked slowly toward the Russian flag that decorated the doorway of the commandant's office.

He barely acknowledged her as she entered, remaining hovered over a stack of papers that were apparently awaiting his signature. The commander glanced up and frowned. He was balding and overweight, sweating profusely even though his office was without heat.

Christina placed her documents before him, then stepped back, waiting as he quickly shuffled through them. The light that hung by a single electrical cord from the ceiling was dim, and it left the Russian's face steeped in shadow.

He swept the papers aside and leaned back in his chair. Still he had not spoken.

"I've come from Hungary," Christina said softly, her throat dry and her voice cracking. "From Budapest."

The commandant's eyes narrowed. He obviously did not want to be bothered, especially by some waif from Hungary, even though he did admire her taste in clothes. The Persian lamb jacket must have cost someone a lot of money, and he did not like anybody these days with a lot of money.

"I would like a visa to Poland." Christina forced a smile that flickered on her lips then faded.

"Denied."

The commandant's voice rang through the empty office like a rifle shot.

"I don't understand."

"It's very simple," the Russian officer snapped. "You are not allowed to go to Poland."

"Why not?"

"It is not under our jurisdiction to say who goes to Poland or who leaves Poland." The commandant leaned forward and propped his elbows on the desk. "Poland now has its own military government, and that government makes its own rules. I do not do that for them."

"But my home is in Poland."

The Russian shrugged. "So my home is in Leningrad. It looks as though neither one of us is where we should be." He dismissed Christina with the wave of his hand.

"Wait," she said. "I have a letter for you. It is from one of your friends. He said that you and he fought side by side when the German army marched against Leningrad." With trembling hands, she laid the wrinkled envelope on the desk before him.

The commandant hesitated for a moment, then opened it. He scanned the words.

Christina held her breath.

He smiled.

She smiled back.

He looked up and slowly wadded the paper into a small, crumpled ball and dropped it at his feet.

"What's wrong?"

"I never heard of him in my life."

"He said you were friends," Christina argued.

"He obviously lied."

"But I must get home. It's been so long, and I want to see my family so badly." Fear knotted in Christina's stomach. "Please let me go back home."

"Visa denied."

Christina felt sick, too weak to stand. She looked around her for a chair. There was none. She held on to the desk for support.

"Then I must return to Budapest." Her words were barely audible. "I shall need papers to return to Hungary."

"Denied."

Christina stared at the commandant with disbelieving eyes. Her shoulders trembled, and there was panic in her voice. "Then where can I go?"

"I don't care as long as it's not Poland or Hungary or the eastern sector of Berlin."

"What will become of me?"

"That is not a problem of the Russian government."

The commandant rose from his chair, picked up a pile of papers and walked briskly toward the doorway. He motioned for a guard to remove the girl from his office.

"You can't just leave me stranded," Christina yelled.

The commandant already had. He never looked back.

Chapter 8

THE YOUNG RUSSIAN GUARD escorted Christina from the gray building and into the cold winds blowing out of a desolate sky. The chill cut through her jacket, and she shivered. Her face was raw, her eyes blurred. She picked up her suitcase and started walking as the mist around Berlin thickened and became rain.

"Miss," the guard suddenly called out, "you must wait a minute."

Christina turned and looked back into a boyish face not yet scarred by the rigors of war.

"Where are you going?" he asked.

She shrugged and gave him a forlorn smile.

"Do you have some place to stay?"

She shook her head.

He reached out and took her hand, and Christina recoiled at his touch. The guard pulled her closer to him.

"I have some place for you to stay," he whispered. "I will keep you warm at night, all night long."

He laughed laconically.

Christina felt his arms tighten around her waist. He pressed his wind-blistered lips against her neck and kissed her, and she jerked away, flushed with anger and fear and nausea. His had become the face of an unleashed animal. Christina gritted her teeth and slapped it.

"You can't hit a Russian soldier," the guard snapped.

She slapped him again, harder this time.

The guard licked his lip and tasted blood, his own. He took one step toward Christina, but her words stopped him cold.

"You're not the first Russian soldier who wanted to have his way with me," she said through clenched teeth. "He tried. He's dead."

"You killed him?" the guard said, feigning fear.

"I didn't have to."

"Then who did?"

"His commanding officer shot him to death."

The bravado disappeared from the young soldier's eyes. He tried to laugh but couldn't. He stepped back toward the gray building, and motioned toward the empty road that wound around the piles of rubble and trash heaps surrounding the heart of Berlin.

"Take it," he said. "See where it leads you. By night, you'll be wishing you could find me. By morning you may be dead."

He threw back his head and laughed again.

Christina grabbed her suitcase and stumbled down the road, and the guard's laughter was a mockery of her despair. She had no idea where she was going or how to get there. She simply ran, bent against the wind, feeling dirty and abused, with only the rain to wash away the tears.

Christina had always pitied the homeless. She had

seen them in Budapest, now in Berlin, walking aimlessly about the city, their faces haggard, their shoulders sagging, their hopes abandoned, their dreams gone. Men with no place to sleep at night, followed by children with nothing to eat. The sight of them had haunted Christina ever since the bombs began falling, leaving them to wander from town to town, to steal from the dead, to survive on the table scraps they could dig out of a rancid garbage can.

She had cried for the homeless.

Now she was one of them.

A taxi driver had returned her to Berlin's western zone, slipping past craters and broken girders, grim, muted testimonies to the destruction that came from the sky. The narrow street was littered with cracked bricks and stones, the scattered remains of Germany's past and present. Ahead Christina saw the crippled towers of the Kaiser Wilhelm Gedachtniskirche, blasted without mercy from the nineteenth century, neo-Romanesque facade of the memorial church. War had stripped away the pride, the dignity of Berlin like a hard, summer blight.

The driver had asked for an address, but Christina hadn't answered.

She sat there, soaked to the skin, her teeth chattering in the late winter's chill, not really knowing whether to feel angry or sorry for herself. Her curls were plastered against her face, and the insides of her shoes were soggy. The wet Persian lamb's wool had begun to smell.

The driver asked again, "What's the address, miss?"

"I don't remember," Christina lied.

"You don't have a place to go, do you?"

"No."

"The British and the French both have place for people like you," he said softly. "Believe me, lady, there are a lot of people out there who don't have anywhere else to go."

The driver had a kindly face, weathered and wrinkled,

partially hidden by a white beard. Once there might have been rage or discontent burning inside of him, too. But those fires, Christina thought, had been smothered out long ago. He looked over his shoulder at her, and there was compassion in his pale blue eyes.

"I'll take you to the British headquarters," he said.

"Why the British?"

He shrugged. "It is closer," he told her.

Christina had virtually marched into the Russian headquarters, calm and confident, not expecting any trouble at all. Obtaining her traveling documents for Poland, she had been assured, was only a formality, one that could be accomplished quickly enough for her to catch the evening train for her homeland. Since then, she had been insulted, accosted, thrown out into the streets, and drenched with rain.

Her courage, as well as her appearance, had wilted.

She timidly approached the British officer in charge, sat on the edge of a straight-backed wooden chair, and quietly told him her story.

He listened intently, nodding in an understanding, fatherly, sort of way. He was, in fact, probably old enough to be Christina's father, a career officer with white hair and a white handlebar mustache whose last tour of duty had brought him to Germany. His uniform was freshly pressed, his boots spit polished and shining like a mirror. Colonel Blair not only liked people, he felt for them. He hurt with them. He knew what suffering was all about. As a soldier, he had seen so much of it in his time.

He stood and reached for a china teapot just behind his desk. "Tea?" the colonel asked. "I've had better, you know, but it might warm you up a bit."

"Please. That's kind of you."

"Not at all." The colonel filled a cup and handed it to Christina. "Cream?"

"No thank you."

"You've had quite a frightful day, my dear," he said,

patting her shoulder. "But you don't have to worry now. We'll do what we can to help you."

Christina's face brightened and she pushed the ringlets away from her eyes.

"Can you help me get home, then?" she asked. The lilt had returned to her voice. "Can you make arrangements for me to get to Poland?"

"I'm afraid not."

"Then I'll have to go back to Hungary." She sighed with a certain amount of bitter resignation.

"I'm afraid that's quite impossible, too."

"I thought you said that you could help me?"

"We'll do all we can," the colonel replied, blowing gently on his tea to cool it. "We can keep you here, give you a nice room and three meals a day." He chuckled. "And, of course, we serve tea twice daily, too. Can't do without it. We've fought wars without ammunition before, but never without our tea."

The colonel's tone grew more serious. "I can understand your plight, my dear. I can make arrangements for you to go almost anywhere you want, with the exception of Poland, Hungary, or even the eastern sector of Berlin. Those are all under Russian occupation, and they won't permit anyone to enter there without their approval. And they don't give their approval to anyone."

Christina slowly shook her head. "I thought the British and the Russians were allies," she said.

"Oh, we are," the colonel admitted. "We're allies. But I'm afraid that we're not very good friends."

"So I'm stuck here?"

The colonel smiled apologetically. "It's not much. Under the circumstances, it's the best we can do."

Christina stood and walked to the window. Outside, beyond the leafless limbs of the trees, almost hidden away in the mist, she saw a cluster of stone buildings connected by walkways and gardens. The courtyard between them was deserted, and she could imagine that in happier times, it would have looked very much like a college campus. The grounds were so serene, surrounded by a lake, untouched by the spoils of war.

"What is this placed called?" Christina asked.

"A Displaced Persons' Camp."

Agony again gripped Christina's heart. She whirled and snapped harshly, "I'm not a displaced person."

The colonel answered her outburst with a sad smile. "For the time being," he said softly, "I'm afraid that we all are. Unfortunately, we have no choice."

Christina followed the Colonel across the grounds toward the building that would be her home, a place among strangers, a refuge for the displaced, the lost, and, she supposed, the dispossessed. She braced her back against the rain, hurrying to keep up with his long strides. Around her, the gateways were guarded by British military police, their faces hard and undaunted by the dreary weather that had fallen upon Berlin. The colonel opened the door for her, and Christina sloshed through the mud and ran quickly inside, pausing to catch her breath in a dimly-lit hallway.

"Second chamber on your left," the colonel told her.

Christina nodded, wiped the rain from her face, and walked uneasily into the room. She was assigned a bed in the far corner, a table, chair, and dresser, and Christina glanced around at the gaunt faces staring back at her. There were ten of them and she wondered if she looked as depraved and misplaced as those women did. Their eyes were glassy, gazing into space, aware that she was in the room, but not quite seeing her.

"Hello," Christina said softly.

No one responded.

She turned around to the colonel. "What's wrong with them?" she asked.

"They have seen too much."

"Where are they going?"

"None of them seem to know."

Christina stepped back against the wall. "They frighten me," she said.

"Don't worry," the colonel assured her. "They're harmless." He shrugged. "I'm afraid they're like you and me and everyone else in Berlin. They're frightened, too. For some of them, the war is over. For some, I don't think it will ever end."

Christina sat down gingerly on her bed and rubbed her hands together to warm them.

"Can I get you anything?" the colonel asked.

"No, thank you. Not now."

A smile lit up his ruddy face. "You'll feel better after you get some dry clothes on," he said confidently, "so don't tarry any in here. It can be a bit drafty in winter, I'm afraid, and you can catch a death of a cold before you know it. There's a bathroom down the hallway where you can towel off."

He looked at his watch, then continued, "It appears that you've missed lunch. But we'll be serving tea in two hours and dinner at eight."

"I'm not hungry," Christina opened her suitcase and rummaged around for a dry dress.

"No one is when they first arrive," the colonel replied. "But there's a good chance that you will be by nightfall. You *have* to eat, even when you're feeling bad for yourself."

Christina started to protest.

The colonel raised his hand to silence her. "That's all right," he said. "We all have our little moments of despair sometime. I get the blues myself, especially when it rains, and around here it's almost always raining."

"But you seem so jolly."

The colonel shrugged. "I'm very good at lying," he whispered, "especially to pretty girls. I sometimes think that it's just part of my military training." His grin broadened. "But don't fret. With some luck, we may have you out of here before you have time to grow too accustomed to this place or my lies."

"Home?"

The colonel's eyes were apologetic. "Someplace better than this, at least."

"I won't go anywhere else but home."

"We'll see."

The door shut gently, and Christina was overwhelmed by the silence around her. People kept staring at her, but no one spoke. No one smiled. The room was bare and gray, just a way station, she thought, for wayward souls, and she was one of them. She picked up her dry dress and walked quickly toward the hallway, and behind her a woman began to cry.

Darkness descended upon Berlin, but Christina could not sleep. She thought of her Uncle Arpad and Aunt Vera. They must think that she had arrived in Poland by now, back in the warmth and the comfort of her own home, safe in the arms of her mother and father. They would be worried sick if they knew she had never gotten out of Berlin. And what about the Russian major who commanded their house? Did he know she would be detained in Berlin? Had he actually believed that she would be given a visa to Poland, or was he merely playing mind games with her? You can never trust a Russian, her uncle had told her one night. Perhaps he was right. The major was a hard man, a strict man. Perhaps he did know what he was doing when he condemned her to be a woman without a country, displaced and distraught.

Christina reached under her pillow and pulled out a wrinkled envelope and read John's letter in the dim glow of the moonlight that drifted through the window. Poor John, she thought. He had promised to come back and find her regardless of whether she stayed in Hungary or fled to Poland. He didn't care. He wanted to see her again and nothing or no one would stop him. That's what he had said. And John Christy was, she was sure, a man of his word. On a whim, she had even written him the afternoon she left Budapest, sending him the addresses of her mother, her grandmother, and her Aunt Sophie in Bydgoszcz. He would look for her. Christina had no doubt about it. John was a crazy American, and crazy Americans had a habit of doing foolish things like that.

But he would never find her, not in Berlin, not in some British concentration camp. Christina looked around at the shadows sleeping beside her. They came from all parts of a war-stricken Europe: Holland, France, Belgium, Italy, Greece, and God only knew where else. Some still clung to dreams that were the curse of the young. Others had given up, having grown too old and too weary to start over again. Most were alone, their families gone, their homes gone, their lives wasted and worthless. Now they had all been thrown together to bide their time in a prison without locked doors. There were no bars on the windows. Christina had been told that she was free to go and come as she pleased, as long as she returned to her room by ten o'clock at night. Yet, she was a prisoner just the same.

The days were all alike.

But the faces kept changing. No one stayed for long. Christina stood at her window and watched one ragged group march away to parts unknown as another ragged group came stumbling into the compound.

There would be a few hours of sleep, a few hot meals, then the stragglers would be herded back down to the railroad yards and packed on trains and carried away. They swarmed back across Europe. Some, Christina hoped, would find their old homes. Some would no doubt build new ones. Some would die as strangers and be buried in unfamiliar soil with no one there to mourn their passing.

On the third day, the colonel called for her.

"You're looking much better," he said pleasantly.

"Thank you."

"I have good news for you."

A smile lit up Christina's face.

"I have arranged passage for you to England."

The smile quavered slightly, then faded.

"I must get back to Poland," Christina replied softly. "Nowhere else. I appreciate what you are doing for me. But I'm tired and I want to go home."

"There is quite a large Polish community in England," the colonel explained patiently. "Most went there before the war. They were the lucky ones. They got out before Hitler's invasion. Perhaps your family was among them. Perhaps you can find them there."

"My father wouldn't leave."

"What makes you so sure."

"He was Polish. He loved his country." Christina's eyes burned with pride. "He wouldn't turn his back on his homeland. He would have stayed and fought."

The colonel shrugged and reached for his teacup. "You must be a lot like him," he acknowledged.

Christina's smile returned. "Thank you," she said. The colonel leaned forward and motioned toward an empty cup. "Tea?" he asked.

"Please."

"Tell me about yourself, Christina," he said as he poured her cup full. "It looks as though you might be here for a long time, so we may as well get to know each other."

Christina took a sip and frowned.

"Too hot?" the colonel asked.

"Too bitter."

The colonel's shrug was an apology. "I'm afraid German water is doing its best to corrupt our good English tea," he said. "But, I guess, bitter tea is better than none at all."

His laughter was contagious.

Christina leaned back and crossed her legs. "I can tell you everything there is to know about me before you finish your tea," she said. "I'm nineteen. I was born in Poland but visiting my aunt and uncle in Budapest when the war broke out. I graduated from the University of Budapest with a pre-med degree, and I always had dreams of someday becoming a doctor."

"I guess the war postponed that dream."

"In a way. The Russians stopped me."

The colonel looked surprised.

"As you know," Christina continued, "when the Russians defeated the German forces in Hungary, they took over control of the country. They would not let me enter medical school unless I signed a paper and joined the communist party."

"And you refused, I presume."

"Of course. I'm not a communist."

"You do have your principles."

"I have my pride." Her voice crackled with resentment. "I will not become something I don't believe in."

The colonel grinned. "You also have a stubborn streak that a hammerhead army mule would envy," he told her with admiration. "It's a good quality to have sometimes, but, I'm afraid, it can also get you in a lot of trouble."

Christina winked. "I'm used to it."

"I bet you are."

The colonel stood, walked around the desk, reached down and took Christina's hand. "Come with me," he said. "I have someone I would like for you to meet. I know that he would certainly like to meet you. I must warn you in advance that he's a little different from the rest of us. He's an American."

"Americans are crazy."

"I know, my dear." The colonel laughed. "That's why I think that you and he will get along so well together."

At the far end of the hallway, Christina was ushered into the private office of Dr. Joseph Smith, a medical officer from Chicago. He looked harried, and the black circles under his eyes revealed an obvious lack of sleep. But he sat patiently and listened while the colonel briefly told him of the circumstances that had brought Christina to the camp.

He glanced up at her. "I understand you speak pretty good English," he said.

"I've studied hard to learn it."

"How's your German?"

"I've been speaking it most of my life." Christina shrugged matter-of-factly. "Of course, for the past few years I've had occasion to speak it quite often."

"You squeamish at the sight of blood?"

Christina held herself rigid, and her eyes hardened as she cut her eyes toward the medical officer. "I have seen a lot of blood," she answered coldly. "I have seen a lot of men bleed, and working in the Budapest hospitals I have held their hands while they died, never knowing which breath would be their last one. I am not squeamish at the sight of blood. I am not afraid of being near death. The screams of dying men do not give me nightmares." She paused. "Do they give you nightmares, doctor? Do they keep you awake at night?"

"Sometimes."

"They trouble me only because I am not able to help them, because I am not able to breathe life back into them."

"You can't perform miracles, even if you're a doctor."

"You can try."

Dr. Smith picked up a stack of folders off his desk and handed them to Christina.

"I need a good medical assistant," he said. "Are you willing to give it a shot?"

"I may not be qualified."

"Maybe not." He grinned. "But you're damn sure tough enough. We got a lot of soldier boys over here in Berlin who are lonesome and bored and still haven't gotten the adrenalin of combat out of their system. They work all week. They get drunk on the weekends. Then we see 'em after they've been beaten or cut or shot or torn up in a car wreck. None of them are ever pretty sights to see. Some of them are American, some are British, and quite a few are German. What I'm looking for is somebody who is fluent in both English and German, who can interpret and translate for me, and who won't go throwing up all over the emergency room just because a little blood gets smeared on them."

Christina studied Dr. Joseph Smith. He was tall, maybe six feet or better, and slender. Hard, frustrating work in a hospital could keep the weight off anyone, she knew. He had a kind face, one that could even be called handsome, and an air of confidence about him that Christina had only found in Americans. There was definitely something about him that Christina liked. Maybe it was his accent. It reminded her of John Christy. Maybe it was the twinkle in his eyes. They laughed even when he didn't. Dr. Joseph Smith, Christina decided, was a man she could trust.

"I can do the job," she said tersely.

"It's not easy."

"I haven't found anything that is."

"The hours are long."

"I have no better way to spend them."

"You don't get much sleep."

"I don't sleep much anymore anyway."

"The drunks can get pretty mean sometime."

"I can handle them."

"They may make a pass or two at you."

"Not while I have a needle in my hand."

"The pay's not much."

Christina sighed. "All I need is enough money to buy a one-way ticket to Poland."

Dr. Smith stood and walked toward the doorway. "Colonel," he said, looking back over his shoulder.

"You're right about one thing."
"What's that?"
"She's stubborn as hell."

Chapter 9

CHRISTINA CHECKED THE BIG CLOCK on the wall, then glanced around her. Midnight was still an hour away, but already the clinic's emergency room was beginning to fill up with the usual assortment of cuts, bruises, and abrasions. Soldiers were a strange breed, she had decided. Most of them had fought a war and survived, dodging bombs and bullets and anything else that the Germans had thrown their way. They had gambled with death, probably cheated, and won. Now, it sometimes seemed to her, they were hell-bent on cramming the rest of their lives into a few short months. They lived fast, loved hard and often, and some of them died needlessly. It was such a waste.

"They're just kids," Dr. Smith had told her. "They go out and drink too much to prove they're men. They chase down every harlot in Berlin so they can feel like men. And they fight because they've been trained to fight, and they don't believe any man would ever back down from a fight."

"They're foolish."

"They're kids."

Christina looked across the crowded room and smiled sadly. So they were, young men not yet in the prime of life, trapped in a foreign land, still scared, and too frightened to admit it.

One had rammed his jeep into a tree on the outskirts of Berlin.

"I'm surprised it didn't kill him," Dr. Smith said without emotion.

Another had his skull cracked. He had been found lying naked and unconscious behind the back stairway of a house of somewhat dubious repute.

"He's also lucky."

"He doesn't look so lucky to me," Christina said curtly, wiping away the blood that had dried on his neck.

"All she took was his money. It could have been worse."

Christina sighed. "Well, maybe he's learned his lesson this time."

"He hasn't."

"What do you mean?"

"He'll go back." Dr. Smith grinned broadly. "They always go back."

"Some of those German girls are leeches." Christina frowned as the final stitches were sewn into place. The soldier groaned. "They hang around with painted smiles and cheap perfume, and sell their love for an hour or for a night. It's disgusting."

Dr. Smith shrugged. "You should have a little sympathy for them," he replied. "Berlin has been torn apart by the Americans and the Russians. Its people are out of work. The economy has fallen apart. There are no jobs, and the GIs have the only money in town. The girls have to do whatever they can do in order to eat and sleep like the rest of us."

Christina grunted. "They spend a lot of time in bed," she spit out. "But they don't ever sleep."

Dr. Smith laughed, and together they moved on to their next case. It was a Saturday night like most Saturday nights in Berlin. The gunshot victim was patched up and sent home. There were two drunks who had passed out on the street. A sergeant from Oklahoma thought he was tough enough to take on the entire military police force. He wasn't nearly as tough as he thought he was. Two soldiers got in a fight over the same woman. One required twenty-six stitches to close up the gash in his face, and he won the fight, or so he said.

He looked up at Christina and grinned his best countryboy grin. "Honey," he said, "I sure wouldn't have been down there if I'd a knowed you was up here."

She ignored him.

"You just about the prettiest little thing I've seen since I've been in Germany. And, believe me, I've been looking around, too."

"You're drunk," she answered dryly.

"God, I hope so." He reached out and took her hand in his. "I ain't gonna be in here all night, honey, and neither are you. Maybe we could go somewhere later."

"Fine," Christina replied.

"You mean it?"

"Of course." She smiled at him caustically. "I'll go home. And you, my boy, can go to hell."

She patted him gently on the cheek and walked away.

"Hey," he yelled, "does this mean you don't love me?"

Christina laughed.

"I could love you." His eyes twinkled, even in pain.

Christina's voice softened. "Forever?" she teased.

The soldier propped himself up on one arm and grinned a crooked grin. "Let's take it one night at a time," he said. He shrugged. "Hell, one night with me might seem like forever."

It had become a nightly ritual. Soldiers came into the medical clinic sick or injured, and hers was the first pretty face they saw smiling at them. Christina joked. She teased. She held their hands when the pain became almost too much to bear. She gently washed the mud and the blood and beer from their faces. To them, she was the girl back home, the fantasy they had dreamed about, the angel of mercy who did what she could to make the pain go away. Some fell in love with her. Some only thought they did. Some begged her to wait for them. A few asked her to marry them.

"I can't," she would say, her eyes twinkling.

"Are you waiting for someone else?"

"No."

"Are you in love with another man?"

"No."

"Is there anyone else in your life?"

"Maybe."

Maybe not. Christina no longer knew. She would go back to her room in the early morning hours, close her eyes, and sometimes think about John Christy. As she lay there alone in the darkness, she could almost make herself believe that one day he would come back to her. After all, he had promised he would, and John Christy was a man of his word. Yet, she also knew that young men who were in love with being in love could not always be held accountable for what they said or what they did. The heart sometimes plays tricks, and their promises are much like the clouds that drift across a summer sky, beautiful today but forgotten as soon as the night comes to chase them away.

Where was John Christy now? At sea? In another port somewhere on the coast of Europe? With another girl? Would he be dancing with her until dawn and toasting her with wine, too? Maybe at this very moment, John was sitting in a hotel room, writing, *I have never known anyone exactly like you. Perhaps there is no one else who could have captivated me so completely with her charm and wit. I shall never be able to forget you, and I won't rest until I have the opportunity to see you again anywhere you might be.* But whose name would be on the letter? Would he be sending her red roses? Would she be foolish enough to sleep with the wrinkled letter under her pillow as Christina had done?

Christina opened her eyes and stared into the darkness. Why did she care what John Christy was doing? She didn't own him. He certainly didn't own her. No one did. She had her own fierce pride and independent spirit. Life had not been fair to her. It had not been fair to a lot of people, and she saw them every day coming and going from the Displaced Persons Camp. Yet, Christina knew she could make it somehow and someday. She didn't need John Christy. She didn't need anyone.

She turned her face to the pillow and wondered if he were thinking of her.

How would he find her?

Would he even try?

The days dragged past, and the skies were squeezed dry of their rain, and the lingering chill of winter reluctantly gave up its grip on the city. The trees around the camp were dressed out in their new leaves, and the gardens were ablaze with the color of spring flowers. Throughout Berlin, the piles of rubble became mountains, great, tragic monuments to war and the spoils of war. Berlin had died a slow death, but the end, when it came, had come quickly and efficiently and completely. The city had been the heartbeat of the Third Reich, drained of its lifeblood on both sides of the Rhine. It had gone out with a bang, not a whimper.

Christina's lifestyle had changed. She had moved from the dormitory of the lost and damned into an apartment shared by three American Red Cross nurses. She was even given a WAC uniform to wear. But whether she liked it or not, Berlin had become home. Others left. She stood in her window and watched them go. She was always the one left behind.

"This is such a godforsaken place," Dr. Smith had told her one night when they walked together into the clinic. "Why don't you get out of here? The stench of war is all over Berlin, and you deserve a lot more out of life."

"Someday I'll leave."

"When?"

"When they let me go back to Poland."

"That might be a long, long time."

"I can wait."

The doctor put a protective arm around her shoulders. "America's a better place to wait, or maybe England," he said.

The doctor was right. Christina knew it. But for some reason she could not bear to leave Berlin, and she didn't really know why.

"I'm needed here," was all she said.

"You're doing a helluva job." Dr. Smith removed his jacket and tossed it over the back of a chair. "For *your* sake, I wish you were somewhere else. For *my* sake, I'm damn glad to have you around."

Christina smiled.

The doctor began washing his hands, waiting for the first casualty of the night to be ushered into the emergency room. War, he understood. The wounded had, at least, been fighting for a country or a cause. Drunken brawls, he often said, were senseless. And the car wrecks sickened him. The more whiskey some kids drank, the faster they drove, and the slower their reflexes became. They got out of synch with themselves, and sometimes it cost them their lives. God, he hated—he dreaded—writing letters to parents and wives, trying—with as much compassion and kindness as possible—to tell them how a stupid, drunken soldier had been needlessly splattered over some German highway. Christina would be better off someplace else, he knew, and so would he.

The GI's right eye was purple and swollen, and his nose had probably been broken. He gritted his teeth as Christina gingerly wiped the dirt and glass shards out of the gash that ran raggedly across his cheekbone.

The soldier flinched.

"Does it hurt?" Christina asked.

"Like hell."

"It looks like you ran your face into a glass wall."

"A beer bottle."

Christina suppressed a grin. "What were you doing?" she asked.

"Playin' poker."

"That sounds harmless enough."

"Adams said I was cheatin'."

"Were you?"

"He said I was."

"You should be more careful." Christina frowned and soaked a piece of gauze with alcohol, then pressed it gently upon the cut. "What you did was a disgrace."

"What? Playin' poker?"

"No." She giggled. "Getting caught."

The soldier laughed with her. "What are you," he asked.

Christina made a face at him. "The last time I looked," she replied, "I was a girl. I thought, perhaps, that you might have already noticed."

The soldier gripped the sides of the table and jerked as the alcohol bit into the raw flesh of his wound. For a moment, his breath came in short, painful bursts, then he relaxed.

"That's not what I mean," he said. "Your accent is different. I know you're not an American, and you don't sound like any German girl I've heard lately. What country did you come from?"

"Poland."

"Really?" The soldier rolled over onto his side so he could see Christina better. "I was in Poland during the last days of the war."

Christina's eyes suddenly widened with excitement. "Did you go near Bydgoszcz?"

The GI shrugged. "Hell if I know," he answered. "I went to a lot of places, but I couldn't pronounce any of them."

"Bydgoszcz is my home."

"Maybe I was there. I don't know."

"Tell me, what does Poland look like? It's been so long since I've seen it, since I was there." She grabbed the GI's hand and squeezed it, eagerness in her voice.

The soldier stared at her for a moment, then turned and looked away. "You can tell they fought a war there," he said softly. "It was hit pretty hard."

"How long were you there?"

"Just a few weeks." Pain cut sharply into his eyes, and it wasn't from the gash on his face. "They sent my company in to clean up Auschwitz." He shuddered and closed his eyes to block out the unholy memory. "I've never seen anything like it before." His voice cracked. "And I don't ever want to see anything like it again."

Christina sat down beside him. "What happened at Auschwitz?" she asked.

"It was a Nazi concentration camp," the GI answered, the life gone from his voice. "They herded prisoners in from all over Europe. They worked 'em. They shot 'em. They gassed 'em in the shower stalls—men, women, and children. It didn't make no difference to the Germans. They might as well have been slaughterin' cattle."

Christina paled. "How many died there?" Her voice was barely a whisper.

"Who knows?" The GI shook his head. "I've heard some reports that say a million, some that say more."

"Jesus . . ." It was a prayer.

"The Nazis killed 'em, then they took 'em out and

burned their bodies. The whole stinkin' place still smells like burnin' flesh. I get sick just thinkin' about it."

Christina's heart ached, and she fought back tears. "What kind of prisoners were taken there?" she asked, afraid to hear his answer.

"Mostly Jews," he said. "That's what I heard. For some reason, Hitler didn't like the Jews. He swore he'd get 'em all, and he damn near did."

"It's horrible." A damp chill seeped into Christina's bones. Her forehead felt wet and clammy.

"They say the screams are what drove everybody crazy. Every day. Every night. There was always somebody in there screaming. At night, they say, if you stand up there in the woods and listen close enough, you can still hear 'em. I didn't try it. I was afraid that I would."

Christina felt faint. She stood and staggered toward the door, holding onto the wall for support. Her legs felt like rubber, and the room had begun to spin. God, she had known war was terrible. She knew that men had died, probably women and children, too. And Poland had suffered the first blow from Hitler's war machine. She remembered Uncle Arpad, leaning over the radio, trying to piece together the reports of the invasion as they came crackling through the static. But Auschwitz? What in God's name had happened at Auschwitz, and why? Auschwitz wasn't war. It was murder, wholesale murder, and why hadn't somebody stopped it? The people of Poland would never stand for anything so hideous taking place within their borders. Poland would have risen up in anger and destroyed Auschwitz. Then reality hit Christina with the impact of a pistol shot. *My God*, she thought, *what had happened to the people of Poland?*

She rushed out into the cool winds of darkness. The doctor found her thirty minutes later, huddled in the far corner of the garden wall, staring with unseeing eyes into the night.

"What's the matter, Christina?" he asked softly.

She did not respond.

He knelt beside her and began slowly rubbing her hands. They were limp and icy. And Dr. Smith saw that the color had been drained from her face.

"What's wrong?" he asked again.

"Auschwitz." Her voice was barely audible.

"It was a terrible place."

"Then you know about it?"

"I've heard stories."

"Tell me they're not true."

"I wish I could, Christina." He took her arm and helped her to her feet. "I wish to God that I could."

Christina was afraid to sleep that night. She knew the nightmares would come if she dared to close her eyes, so she walked in the courtyard until the first pale streaks of a new morning were etched in the sky. The sunshine would cheer her up. It always did. The sunshine went awry.

When the gates opened, Christina followed the crowd out of the camp, and for hours she wandered, not realizing that she was on the back streets of Berlin. When she was conscious of where she was, she knew she shouldn't be there alone. At that moment, she no longer cared. She walked as if in a trance, trying to sort out the confusion, the fear, the uneasiness that gnawed at her mind.

Maybe the soldier was exaggerating, Christina thought. Soldiers were always exaggerating the truth. Besides, it was ridiculous to think that as many as one million people would have calmly allowed themselves to be killed in a prison camp without revolting. Countries launched full-scale wars sometimes without an army that big. Besides, Christina had always been taught that people were basically good and God fearing, and no God fearing man, regardless of how mad, would be so heartless as to execute that many people. Auschwitz, she assured herself, had probably had its share of suffering. And some no doubt had died there. But it couldn't have been as horrible as the GI had told her. No place on earth could. Dr. Smith had simply said it was terrible. But then, all prison camps in time of war are terrible. She wouldn't worry about Auschwitz anymore, Christina decided. And the sun, at last, broke through the angry clouds that threatened Berlin.

Christina found herself in the black market shopping area of Tiergarten near the Brandenburg gate. A person could buy almost anything for a price, usually cheap and usually stolen. Christina had heard about the market from the three Red Cross nurses who shared her room.

"You get great bargains," she had been told. "You just pay your money and ask no questions, and nobody ever bothers you. The jewelry is fabulous, and the shoes are the best you can buy. They're imported straight out of Italy."

"Then I must go there sometime."

The nurse had turned away from the mirror and said with feeling, "I certainly wouldn't go there alone. Those guys who stole the stuff once just might sell it to me, then kill me and get it back. That's probably how they got it in the first place."

Christina had laughed. American women, she sometimes thought, were as crazy as American men.

"Besides," she was told, "the Russians have a real nasty habit of raiding the black market everytime they want something and don't want to pay for it."

"The Russians have a lot of nasty habits."

"I'd hate to wind up in their prison."

"Why would they arrest one of us?" Christina had wanted to know.

"Look, sister," the nurse answered, "It's illegal to sell the stuff. It's illegal to buy it. If you're there, the Russians figure you're guilty, especially if you're a pretty girl. The Russians like pretty girls. And I've heard they like to hurt 'em, too. That's why the German whores stay as far away from the Russian sector as they can. Oh, I'm sure they would turn you loose after awhile. But you certainly wouldn't be the same girl when you left that you were when you went in."

Christina glanced around the square. It was early, but already the vendors were at work, hundreds of them, all smiling and waving, trying to attract the attention of any potential buyer who chanced into the Tiergarten. As far as she could see, there were rows of jewelry and silver, crystal and china, clothes and shoes. Some were stacked on tabletops, others placed on faded blankets. The prices were cheap. By night, they would be even cheaper. Men and women didn't eat unless they sold, and some were feeling hunger pains that were several days old.

Christina was engulfed with a cacophony of voices, loud and growing louder, and they drew her closer toward an odd, melancholy marketplace where women with rags on their feet sold merchandise that was surely worth a fortune. To Christina, it didn't make sense.

"Nothing makes sense anymore," the lady with aging eyes and a cracked German accent told her. "Look around you. Some of these people—before the war—were thieves, and they are still thieves. Some were businessmen, but they no longer have any jobs, so they smuggle whatever they can smuggle in, and sell it for whatever profit they can get out of it. And some of us?" she shrugged. Her face was tired and gaunt, and her clothes hung loosely on her frail body. "Some of us simply come down to sell our family heirlooms."

"That's so sad," Christina interrupted.

"Not as sad was watching your children go hungry," the woman replied.

"I'm sorry."

"We're all sorry." Her face was full of disgust, and she spit into the dirt at her feet.

Christina couldn't take her eyes off the woman. There was something different about her. She was selling in the German marketplace. But she didn't sound German.

There was a deep seated fear reflected in her face, and her eyes kept darting around the Tiergarten like a trapped animal. She looked as though she felt out of place, an interloper who might get caught at any minute. Perhaps, Christina thought, it had been the trials of war that had turned her hair silver long before its time, that had left her fair skin creased with wrinkles. Perhaps not.

Christina leaned forward and lowered her voice. "You're not German, are you?"

The woman nervously bit her lip and looked frantically around her. No one else was listening. The vendors beside her were all lost in the frenzy of their own activity.

"No," she whispered as she cast her eyes downward and looked away. "Who are you? Why do you want to know?" Her tone had become suddenly defensive.

"Don't be afraid," Christina assured her. "It's just there's something so familiar about your accent."

"I'm from Poland," the woman answered as though it were an apology.

Christina reached down and gently took her wrinkled hand. *Jak sie mos* (How are you?), she said softly.

A smile exploded on the woman's face, and her eyes shone brightly again. She squeezed Christina's hand tightly. *Jak sie mos*, she answered.

Christina felt like laughing, and she felt like crying, so she did a little of both. It had been so long since she had heard her native tongue, and there had been and were times when she was afraid she would never hear it again.

The woman's name was Irena Skiorski, she said, and she and her family lived in the French sector of Berlin. They had fled when the Nazi war machine stormed across Polish borders, and now her husband was an engineer on a train that departed the Russian zone twice a week, bound for Poland.

"Tell me about my homeland," Christina urged.

Sadness returned to the woman's eyes. "It's not the same," she murmured. "It may never be the same again."

"What happened to Poland?"

Irena Skiorski glanced up as she heard the brakes squealing on the outer fringe of the Tiergarten. A siren wailed, and a disturbed tension could be sensed across the marketplace.

A man shouted.

A gun fired.

Then another.

A woman screamed.

"Oh, my God." Irena fell to her knees.

"What's wrong?"

"The Russians. They've come again."

Christina whirled around and saw the trucks plowing into the square, moving steadily forward, taking out anything or anyone who could not escape their wheels. A jeep tore madly into the Tiergarten, as armed troops fanned out and charged into the marketplace.

Screams echoed down the streets.

Then curses.

An old German, too stubborn to run, or maybe he was simply too tired, stood in front of the jeep, his arm raised in open defiance.

The Russian officer shot him dead, once through the forehead, neatly and quickly and without remorse.

Irena scrambled to her feet, grabbed her heirlooms, and swept them into a worn, woolen blanket, dragging them after her as she stumbled into the chaos and confusion of the raid.

"Run!" she yelled at Christina.

The jeep was bouncing closer toward them. Christina reached for the blanket. "Let me help you," she yelled.

Irena jerked away. "Run," she ordered. "For God's sake, don't let them catch you."

Christina heard the jeep grinding its way through the frenzied crowd, scattering people and boxes and tables out of its way, littering the street with silver jewelry and broken china. There was harsh laughter amidst the screams, and a child was crying.

There was a rifle shot.

The bullet kicked up cement and dust at her feet.

A man groaned and pitched forward, face down in the dirt.

The screaming became contagious.

And Christina heard the jeep squeal to a halt. She didn't look back.

She ran.

"Stop!" The command came in Russian.

Christina didn't.

She kept running, shoved forward, then knocked down by frightened forms with frightened faces who all seemed to be moving in all directions at once and going nowhere. She crawled out of the square and bolted toward an alleyway that led behind the hollow hull of a bombed-out building.

"Stop!"

The rifle fired again.

A woman kept screaming, and she wouldn't stop, and it wasn't until Christina had fallen into the shadows that she realized the screams were coming from her own throat.

Chapter 10

THE SHADOWS WERE HER HIDING PLACE. Christina lay in them, pressed against a crumbling brick wall, until the tumult and the shouting had died away in the square. Voices had been silenced, and she heard the whining, complaining engines of the trucks fade away in the distance.

She waited, afraid to move, almost afraid to breathe.

She waited for the Russian officer to find her.

He stood at the entrance to the alleyway, then casually leaned against the wall and calmly lit a cigarette. Christina couldn't see his face, only his eyes, and they burned as red as coals in the dim afternoon light. His arm hung limply at his side, clutching a pistol. He suddenly raised it to shoulder level and fired. The bullet blasted through a garbage can and riccocheted along the bricks and into the gutter.

Now it was the Russian officer's turn to wait.

He stared intently into the alley.

Nothing moved.

He took one step into the darkness, hesitated for a moment, then backed away. Apparently satisfied that the girl had eluded him or was dead, the officer turned abruptly and strode back out into the turmoil that ran rampant throughout the ruins of the marketplace, pausing just long enough to reach down, pick up a silver pendant from the street, and thrust it into his pocket.

Christina watched him climb arrogantly into his jeep, reload his pistol, then ride away, cutting back across the tattered remnants that had been left in disarray throughout the square.

Her knee hurt where she had fallen. It was swollen slightly and the bruise was beginning to turn purple. She limped back out into the Tiergarten as, one by one, the vendors cautiously returned to salvage what they could of their merchandise. Christina searched among them for a glimpse of Irena Skiorski, but all she saw was the haunted, beaten faces of strangers who had nothing left, who had been cast adrift in a world that made no sense. It wasn't the world they had made, simply the one they had inherited.

For them, she knew, there would be no escape.

Christina vowed to find one.

Somehow.

Some way. She would go home again.

On Monday afternoon, Christina left her shift at the medical clinic early. It had been a slow, rather calm and uneventful day for the American forces in Berlin. Some no doubt had gotten into trouble, but they had at least found a way to get into and out of it without getting themselves hurt, and that was all that mattered to Christina. All day, she had been absorbed in her own thoughts, performing her duties with mechanical precision, not really thinking at all about what she was doing. Her mind was on Irena Skiorski, her one fragile link with Poland.

Christina stopped by the American PX, bought a bag of groceries, and persuaded an off-duty medical corpsman to drive her into the French sector of Berlin. It had not been hard. He was lonely. He was looking for company. And she needed a ride. All it took was a smile.

He parked beside a row of tiny flats and killed the engine. "Are you sure this is the right neighborhood?"

"Yes, I think so."

"I don't like the looks of it." The corpsman looked down the deserted street and frowned. It was littered with wind-blown trash.

"Don't worry about me." Christina patted his shoulder. "I know where I'm going. I have a friend who lives here."

"Male or female?"

Christina laughed.

"I'm not sure I should leave you here," the corpsman told her. "It doesn't look like the kind of place a girl like you needs to be wandering around in by herself, especially after dark. There are men in this city who'd give animals a bad name. They got no morals, no scruples, no respect for women of any kind, especially the good-lookin' ones."

Christina eased out of the jeep. "You're a gentleman for worrying about me," she said. "Thank you. But I'll be all right. Believe me."

"I'll wait for you."

"That won't be necessary."

"Maybe for you it's not," he said and grinned. "But for me it is."

Christina cocked her head, arched an eyebrow, and teased, "You better be careful. Somebody may attack you before I get back."

The corpsman's grin broadened. He reached down and patted the .45 pistol that hugged his hip. "I'd like that," he growled. "I'd like that a helluva lot."

"But what if it's a woman?"

He leaned back in his seat, crossed his arms, and stretched out, propping his feet on the dashboard. "I'll be through by the time you get back," he promised.

"It may not take me long."

His grin was an impervious one. "Yeah." He shrugged. "I may have the same problem."

Christina blushed and hoped he hadn't seen her. She turned on her heels and, holding firmly to the bag of groceries, she walked briskly down the sidewalk. She thought she heard the corpsman whistle, long and low, and wondered if he were foolish enough to be whistling at her.

It was rude, but that's the way GIs were.

She knew that a real lady would be angry with him, and it troubled her because she wasn't mad at all.

Christina climbed the rotting steps that led to the front door of a small flat. She knocked and waited. There was no sound from inside, no sign of movement at all. She knocked again and glimpsed a pair of eyes staring at her from behind a ragged window curtain that had once been green and white. Now the colors had faded into one, and it was much too threadbare to ever keep out a summer sun.

The eyes disappeared back into the darkness of the room. Christina knocked again.

The door cracked open.

"*Jak sie mos,*" Christina said softly, and the crack in the doorway widened.

"Why are you here?" Irena Skiorski asked. She looked past Christina and out into the empty street as though she expected to find someone else there. War had taught her to be cautious, and that was why she was still alive. She trusted no one, not even a young oval-faced, curly-haired girl who spoke to her in Polish. She had seen others tricked. She had seen others die. Irena's voice trembled.

"Why are you here?" she repeated.

Christina handed her the bag of groceries. "I brought you these."

Irena's eyes brightened, then became suspicious again. "Why would you do this for me?"

"I guess I'm looking for a friend." Christina groped for words. "And I hoped you would be one," she said.

Irena's gaze swept past the doorway and into the street, searching for any trace of movement that shouldn't be there. It was empty. The wind had died away, leaving the trash where it lay. A gray cat with piercing eyes leaped atop a wooden fence, stared back for a moment, then was gone.

The woman took Christina's arm and pulled her into the flat, quickly shutting the door and locking it. She carried the grocery sack to a small table in the next room where her husband was seated.

"This is the girl from Poland I was telling you about." she said.

He nodded.

"Hello," Christina said softly.

The silence around them was awkward, almost overbearing. Skiorski was a heavy-set man, dressed only in his khaki pants and stained undershirt. He had not bothered to shave that day, and there was a scowl on his face. Like his wife, he did not trust strangers who suddenly appeared at his front door.

"How do you know where we live?" he asked.

"I followed your wife home from the Tiergarten market yesterday," Christina replied. "She didn't see me. I made sure of it. I didn't try to approach her because you never know who's watching, and I didn't want to endanger either one of you."

"Or yourself."

Christina smiled. "I guess we all have to be cautious these days," she said.

"The Russians are worse than the Germans," Skiorski replied bitterly. "Barbarians lost the war. Barbarians won it. They both put their boots on the neck of Poland and tried to break it."

"And succeeded."

"No!" Skiorski yelled.

"But Poland surrendered."

"Poland lost her young men and her old men. But Poland never gave up hope." His eyes flickered with pride that had been tempered for a long time. "I know," he said. "I take my train to Poland twice every week. It's people have been butchered. Their land has been taken from them. The Germans stole it. The Russians won't give it back. But no one has given up. The government surrendered, but the people never will, not as long as they have one last breath within them."

There was controlled violence in his voice.

"Take me with you."

Christina's words startled him.

"What?"

"Take me with you." Christina sat down beside him and put her hand on his shoulder. "Take me back to Poland."

Skiorski's voice softened. "Do you have a visa?"

"No. The Russians won't give them one."

"Then it's impossible."

"You can hide me on the train."

"It's too risky."

"I don't care."

"If the Russians find you, you could wind up dead." He paused. "Or worse."

"I'll take that chance."

Skiorski sighed and stared across the table, unable to free himself from Christina's unwavering gaze. Her eyes were deep-set with determination, her voice steady and calm. He was not dealing with a child, no matter how young she looked to him. Her nerves were probably on edge. So were his. But she wouldn't go to pieces if anything went wrong. He could see it in her face. Skiorski seemed to know, perhaps by instinct, that nothing, short of death, would prevent Christina from some day returning to her homeland. Her mind was made up. No one could change it.

Throughout the evening, he listened to the girl's story. It was sad. But he had heard sad stories before. His own life had been one. Maybe that's why he sympathized with her. Skiorski knew the frustration of being torn apart from a land he loved. He knew what it was like to hurt.

He stood and paced the floor, not daring to look at either Christina or his wife. He caught a glimpse of his reflection in the window and slowly shook his head. He must be looking, he told himself, at the face of a mad man.

"If I find a way to smuggle you into Poland," Skiorski said haltingly, "then you're on your own."

Christina caught her breath.

She thought she was going to scream.

Or maybe cry.

"Thank you," was all she said, and she felt relief and happiness bubbling up within her until she thought it would boil over. Christina grabbed Skiroski and hugged his neck. Then she hugged Irena. She wanted to run out into the street, throw her head back, and shout it to the whole world. She was, at last, going home.

It would be the most difficult secret she ever kept.

"There are no promises," Skiorski said.

"Thank you for trying." Christina was breathless.

"I'll do what I can."

"When can we leave?"

"We'll get word to you." Skiorski rubbed his chin and studied the situation, approaching it in his mind from every angle. "I won't know for sure until the night we depart," he said. "When you hear that there's a rainbow in the sky, then you'll know the time has come."

"And what if I don't hear anything?"

Skiorski grinned and ran a thick hand through his black hair. "Then you'll know the train's not running anymore."

For two weeks, Christina waited and grew more impatient with each passing day. She was tempted, time and again, to make contact with Irena Skiroski and find out what the delay was all about. She was afraid though, to do anything that might arouse suspicion or anger the man who had agreed to take her out of Berlin. His approval was tenuous at best. Skiorski obviously didn't like the idea of smuggling her across the border.

"The place is crawling with Russian guards day and night," he had told her. "Everyone is checked and double checked. Without the proper papers, no one gets into Poland, and no one gets out."

"You can hide Christina in the baggage car," Irena had decided. "No one will find her there."

"I hope not." Skiorski's face had darkened noticeably. Was it worry? Or fear. "A month or so ago, I heard about a Polish soldier who got caught trying to sneak back into the country. He had disguised himself as a priest, but I don't guess he fooled anybody. The Russians arrested him and shipped him off to a prison camp."

"What happened to him?"

"He was tried." Skiorski sighed. "He was shot to death."

Christina didn't flinch.

"But he was a soldier," she insisted.

"It didn't matter."

Each morning, Christina convinced herself that this would be the day when she heard about a rainbow in the sky. No word came. And it was becoming much more difficult for her to believe that a rainbow even existed at all. Her spirits had soared so high. Now they had crashed. She seldom spoke to anyone anymore, and she found more time than she needed to be alone.

She simply did her job, then went back to the apartment.

And waited.

Maybe something had happened to Skiorski, she worried. Maybe he had lied to her. Maybe he had already forgotten his promise to her. Maybe the train wasn't running anymore.

Christina rarely slept.

Her complexion paled, and Dr. Smith was concerned about the dark circles under her eyes. She had only been a wisp of a girl anyway, and now she was losing weight.

"I'm afraid you aren't feeling well," he told her.

"I'll be fine."

"Why don't you take some time off."

Christina forced a smile. "I don't know what I'd do with myself."

"Get away from your troubles before they get you down." Dr. Smith grinned. "Go take in a movie. Watch somebody else try to solve their problems, and it just might help you forget all about yours."

He took her jacket from the closet and wrapped it around Christina's shoulders. "You spend too much of your time these days taking care of everybody else in the clinic," he said, seriously. "I think it's time you took care of yourself for awhile."

Christina started to argue.

"Don't." The doctor winked. "Now get out of here and don't come back until you're feeling better."

Christina choked back a tear. He was a good friend. He cared about her. Outside of John Christy, he just might be the kindest, gentlest man she had ever known. Yet Dr. Joseph Smith didn't really understand. Nobody did.

He would never see her happy again.

For Christina, there would be no happiness until she felt the rumble of that train surging through the night, rolling across the Polish countryside.

She had waited so long.

She was tired of waiting for the rainbow.

Christina walked out of the clinic, and a sudden chill cut through her like a knife. She felt more depressed than she ever had in her whole life.

The afternoon was bathed in sunshine, but Christina did not notice. She only saw the dark clouds, even when there were none in the sky. For a time, she drifted aimlessly through the bombed-out ruins of the city, feeling sorry for herself and ashamed of it. And finally Christina grew tired of the self-pity that dogged her footsteps and decided to take the doctor's advice. After all, she had nothing else to do.

Christina slipped into the movie house that sat on the corner near the clinic and found herself a seat on the back row. The theater was full. It was always full of GIs who were off duty and killing time between assignments. Usually there was so much shouting and cursing amid the wild, at times drunken laughter, so that it was virtually impossible for anyone to hear what was happening on the screen. It didn't matter. The GIs were good at making up their own dialog, and it was always off color and obscene even when the movie wasn't.

But today was different.

An uneasy silence pervaded the blackened interior of the theater. No one talked. No one moved.

The film had already begun.

It was black and white.

And grainy.

And hypnotic.

There was no sound.

Only horror.

Christina heard herself gasp.

On the screen, naked men and women, skeletons who had not yet died, trod upon a frozen ground, their eyes hollow, their faces gaunt, their children running at their feet and crying out.

No one heard.

They were crying silent tears.

Above them hung a sign upon which was written in German:

ARBEIT MACHT FREI. WORK FOR YOUR FREEDOM.

Auschwitz.

My God, Christina thought, it's footage from Auschwitz.

Black and white.

Grainy.

And real.

Her heart pounded wildly, and for a moment she thought it might stop or burst through her chest. She sat transfixed, unable to take her eyes off the naked men and women who stumbled so sadly into the woods, robbed of their last shred of human dignity.

No one fought back. They simply died.

In silence.

Men and women and children, condemned and beyond tears, and no sound came from their lips.

Only silence.

Auschwitz.

A death trap.

Auschwitz.

A hell without hope, where the spirit died long before the soul.

In silence.

God, Christina thought, I can't stand the silence. Won't somebody cry out?

Only the children, tired, ragged, and frightened. Only the children dared to cry out.

And no one heard.

They marched onward, the nameless, the unmourned, to the firing squads, to the gas chambers, to the crematoriums that were ablaze with their ashes.

They were the experiments.

They were the chosen.

Old faces. Young faces. Worn out faces. Jewish faces. Their lives had no meaning.

Death was out of control, moving slowly, moving swiftly, always moving, always silent, day and night without rest.

An old man smiled.

He had no teeth.

A lampshade set in a Gestapo office.

It was made from human skin.

A woman reached for her child. She held him tightly. They would die together.

In silence.

In the showers.

The corpses were piled high, their eyes open, horror forever masked upon their faces.

Men.

And women.

And children.

God, why must there be the children?

Auschwitz.

Poland.

Christina couldn't take it anymore. She bolted from her seat, sick at her stomach, and ran into the lobby. She made it as far as the front door, and then the world turned upside down on her, and Christina fainted dead away. She was unconscious by the time she hit the floor.

When Christina awoke, it seemed to her that she was adrift in a world somewhere far, far away, beyond the touch of reality, lost in a maze of her own thoughts, none of which made any sense to her. The room was so big, and she was so small and insignificant, and the bed kept floating but never went anywhere. She tried to catch the wall and keep it from revolving around her head, but Christina couldn't raise her arms. They were too heavy, and she was too weak.

And the glare of the light in her face was blinding her.

In the distance, Christina heard the faint, unmistakable voice of Dr. Joseph Smith, but she couldn't understand what he was saying, and that troubled her. His words just didn't hang together, and they grated on her nerves. All he did was keep patting her shoulder and speaking to her in an unknown tongue, and Christina wanted to scream. She kept staring at the needle in his hand and couldn't understand why it hadn't hurt when he jammed it into her arm.

Nothing was quite in focus.

The colors drifting around her were all pastels, pale and translucent, ringed with shadows that kept growing larger and darker and blotting out her vision of the room and the doctor who was moving in slow motion, sometimes smiling and sometimes laughing, always in silence.

God, Christina thought, how she hated the silence.

And she couldn't escape it.

Christina's groggy mind finally comprehended what was happening to her. She should have known. She had spent too many days, too many hours in the clinic not to know, and that angered her.

Sedation.

Christina fought it.

Dr. Smith had told her to rest, to take it easy, to take care of herself.

Now she had no choice. He and that damnable needle of his had made sure of it.

Christina's eyes were heavy and dimmed with sleep. The room began to float, and she floated within it. It was dark now, all in shadow, all a blur.

"Is she asleep yet?" Dr. Smith asked his nurse.

"I think so."

"Good." He signed her chart and yawned as he started for the door. "Christina needs all the rest she can get. She pushes herself too hard, and she's let herself get a little rundown."

"She looks healthy enough."

"Physically, she'll be all right. But Christina's suffered a lot of disappointments in her time. It looks like the emotional strain of it all finally just caught up with her and said slow down."

The nurse smiled simply because the doctor expected her to smile and dutifully straightened the sheet around Christina's shoulders.

"When should I schedule her next shot?" she asked.

"Let's see how she's feeling in the morning before we make that decision," Dr. Smith answered. He paused in the open doorway, rummaged around in his shirt pocket, and pulled out a wrinkled piece of paper, frowning slightly as he read it again. "One other thing," he said. "This message came in for Christina late this afternoon, and I'd like for you to give it to her when she wakes up."

For a moment, Christina drifted out of her unconscious state. The doctor's words were still faint, but clearer now, coming from a warped record, it seemed, that was being deliberately played at the wrong speed and volume.

"What's it about?" the nurse asked.

"Something about a rainbow." He shook his head, folded the paper and handed it to her. "It says here that a rainbow will be in the sky tomorrow morning."

"What does that mean?"

"Damned if I know."

Without bothering to look at it, the nurse stuck the hand-scrawled message into the pocket of her uniform and followed the doctor out into the hallway.

On her bed, Christina fought desperately to regain use of her muddled senses. Through the dense fog that surrounded her brain, she had heard the word that she had been hoping for, the magic word. *Rainbow.*

It would be in the sky.

Rainbow.

Tomorrow.

But it wouldn't wait for her. Rainbows never did.

Christina struggled to push herself upright in the bed, and the room started spinning again.

She gritted her teeth.

Damn the room, she thought.

Christina swung her legs over the edge of the bed and frantically shook her head to clear away the cobwebs that lingered there. She took a deep breath, slipped out of the white hospital gown, and reached for her blue dress that had been thrown rather hastily across the dresser.

She stood on uneasy legs and blinked her eyes hard and often to keep the room in focus.

How late was it?

Christina had lost track of time.

Was it too late?

Outside her window, she saw the scattered lights of Berlin glittering in the night.

How long had she been sleeping?

How long would the rainbow remain in the sky before it vanished forever?

Christina knew that perhaps she had one chance to get back to Poland.

This was it. Or had it already passed her by?

She took one awkward step and almost fell, grabbing the wall to steady herself, pressing her face against the cool plaster as she inched her way toward the door.

Only a few more feet to go, she thought.

Easy now.

Then she was in the hallway, dimly-lit and deserted, walking shakily toward the ladies bathroom. It would be a simple climb through the window, she told herself, and she would be gone before anyone had missed her.

The floor beneath her bare feet began to sway, then roll to one side. Her mind raced wildly and suddenly out of control. She saw faces in the shadows, and the faces were grinning at her, or were they snarling?

She had to get away.

If Joseph Smith saw her, he would stop her. He would keep her there. He would not understand.

He would not let her go.

But she must get away. Now. There was no time left to waste. Christina looked down the hallway, and it stretched before her without end, and the walls were closing in around her. The faces in the shadows kept laughing, kept whispering her name, and the lights flickered.

Christina slapped herself, and the sudden, sharp pain temporarily cleared her head. She pitched headlong through the door and into the bathroom, lying for only a moment in the darkness, then crawling toward the pale stars that were barely visible beyond the opening above the radiator.

The wind was warm against her face, and the salt from sweat stung her eyes as Christina threaded her way through the window and tumbled onto the soft, moist dirt of a berm where the grass had been washed away by the rains.

Christina looked up into the black, foreboding sky above her and laughed with the faces in the shadows.

It was indeed, she thought, a good night, a perfect night for a rainbow.

She pulled herself to her feet and stumbled drunkenly down the berm and toward the backstreet that led to her small apartment. Her head throbbed as though it would crack, and a chill probed her spine. Christina felt flushed, and the muscles in her long, slender legs had turned to rubber, threatening to give way with every step. It wouldn't be much longer now, she kept telling herself.

Tomorrow she would be home.

By the time the nurse discovered the empty hospital room, Christina had been driven by taxi to the bad side of Berlin, and she was knocking on Skiorski's door. He found her lying on the porch, crumpled beside her suitcase and asleep.

Chapter 11

THE BLACK COFFEE BURNED Christina's throat. It was so thick she could almost chew it, so bitter she almost spit it out. By the time she had downed the third cup, however, Christina was beginning to view the world around her with clearer eyes. The confusion, the distortions that clouded her mind had been washed away.

She coughed, wiped her mouth, and set the porcelain cup back onto the table.

"We didn't think you were coming," Irena said softly. Her faded yellow robe was pulled tightly around her pudgy body, and her hair hung uncombed around her shoulders.

"I was hoping you wouldn't." Skiorski had a terrible dread on his face. "It's still not too late for you to back out." His eyes were tired, and his hands shook as he lifted a cup of black coffee to his mouth.

"No." Christina had made up her mind long ago. "I'm going. Nothing can stop me now."

"Only the Russians."

Christina ignored him. "What time is it?" she asked.

Skiorski glanced at his watch. "Two o'clock." There was a note of resignation in his voice. "The train leaves in four hours."

"I'll be on it."

Skiorski laughed. "You're as stubborn as an old mule in a new garden." he said. He poured himself another cup, then asked, "Did you bring what I asked you to?"

Christina nodded. She opened her suitcase, pulled out a bottle of whiskey and two cartons of American cigarettes, and gave them to the man.

A smile replaced the scowl on his face. He cradled the bottle gingerly in his thick, grease-stained hands, and breathed a sigh of relief. "These will do just fine," he said as he walked out of the room.

"There's not much time left," Irena told her. "And there's still a lot to be done." She looked at Christina and frowned. "You sure can't leave Berlin looking like that."

"What do you mean?"

"Your clothes are much too nice. They would arouse suspicion before you ever got out of the railroad station." Irena hurried out of the room and returned a moment later carrying a dress and a coat that were worn and threadbare, held together by patches. She handed them to Christina. "These will work much better," she said.

"What if they don't fit?"

"It doesn't matter." Irena's voice had grown cold and metallic, hurried. "Now give me everything important that you are carrying with you."

A frown creased Christina's brow. "Why?" she asked.

"I want to make sure that you still have it all with you when you reach Poland."

For the next thirty minutes, Irena carefully sewed Christina's money, documents, and jewelry into the lining of the old, tattered coat.

"You can't put them in your suitcase," she explained. "The Russians may take your suitcase away from you, even if you reach Poland without being detected. They're scavengers. They're vultures. They prey on everybody and take everything they can get their hands on." Irena looked up and snapped, "Just don't let them get their hands on you." She paused, then asked softly, "Do you have a weapon of any kind?"

"No." Christina shivered.

From inside a drawer beside the stove, Irena produced a small pistol and placed it in Christina's right hand. "It's old," she said. "It has one bullet. If you need it, use it quick and use it wisely." Irena sighed and shook her head in disgust. "Just remember, a Russian man or a Russian jail is worse than death."

"I can't do that," Christina protested.

"You never know what you can do or can't do until you have to do it." She patted Christina's shoulder gently and wiped a tear from her eye. "I wish I had known you longer," Irena said. "I wish I were going with you."

"Why don't you?" Christina was on her feet, a renewed burst of energy in her voice.

"There's nothing left for me in Poland except memories. Here, I can remember the good times. There, I am reminded only of the bad ones."

"I shall miss you." Christina hugged Irena. "And I shall always be thankful for what you and your husband are doing for me."

"Godspeed," Irena's voice cracked. "And God bless you, child. It's too late for some of us to do anything about this life that fate has given us. I only pray that you young people can build a new one and not make the same dreadful mistakes that we did."

Shortly before four o'clock, Christina slipped back out into the darkness and walked alone, dirty and ragged, down the street toward the ravaged steeple of a small

Catholic church that rose up along the outskirts of the French sector. Her shoulders were bent, her head bowed against the wind. Her clothes, much too large, hung crookedly around her, and a black scarf, faded and wrinkled, hid her disheveled hair. To anyone who might have chanced to see her, Christina looked for all the world like one of those poor peasant women who drifted among the streets at night, searching garbage cans for a bite to eat and sleeping in doorways or anywhere they could find shelter against the elements. They were the nameless ones, ignored by Berlin. Christina walked unnoticed into the church.

It smelled of burning wax and was illuminated only by candles that lined the left side of the alter. Smoke from the war had damaged its stone walls, and a bomb had taken away the rectory that once joined the building. Misshapen boards and rubble had been shoved against the church to cover an ugly, gaping hole and keep the rest of the wall from collapsing. Christina crossed herself and knelt beneath the wooden crucifix, the only survivor of the blast.

Her prayer was a simple one.

Divine guidance was what she needed most. That was always what she needed most, and she had never been bashful about asking for it, especially not now in the candleglow of a Berlin night.

And Lord, she pleaded. *give me a safe journey.*

Keep your hand on me and your eyes on Skiorski. Protect him. He's done so much to protect me.

And keep your loving arms around my family.

I miss them so.

I want to see them so badly.

It's been so long since I've heard them say they love me, and I know they do, and I love them so much.

Thank you for Dr. Smith.

Don't forget Uncle Arpad and Aunt Vera. They must be worried sick.

She paused and spent a few moments in silent meditation.

Then suddenly she said, without quite knowing why, *and Lord, bless John Christy, wherever he is.*

Amen.

A hand touched her shoulder.

"It's time."

Christina recognized the harsh voice of Skiorski and nodded without ever looking up.

Together, they walked in silence out of the church, Christina carrying her own suitcase. Two blocks away, they boarded an S-bohn and rode it beneath the Berlin ruins toward the railroad yards. An old man sat sleeping in the corner of the subway car. A companion stared with hollow eyes out into the night, the smell of cheap whiskey on his breath.

Christina started to speak.

Skiorski shook his head. "Not now," he said. Skiorski trusted no one and found that he got along much better that way. Old men have big ears, he told himself. Old men who appear to be sleeping are sometimes not sleeping at all. And drunks are not always drunk.

The S-bohn lurched to a sudden stop and Skiorski was on his feet. The door swung open, and he grabbed Christina's arm, pulling her from the car.

"We'll get off here and walk the rest of the way," he said. "You never know this time of morning whether the Russian guards will be meeting the S-bohn at the station or not. I don't want to take any chances."

He removed the old woolen coat that had been hiding his engineer's uniform and stuffed it into a garbage can. "Follow me," he said quietly, and Skiorski darted into the shadows of an alleyway that ran behind a row of abandoned warehouses. In the near distance, the lonely whistle of a slow-moving train broke the stillnesses of the night.

Christina was amazed. She had never seen Skiorski so

well dressed. His uniform was starched and pressed, and the usual two-day stubble on his face had been shaved clean. In the moonlight, he looked almost dashing, moving quickly, with authority, toward the railroad station.

At the edge of the last warehouse, Skiorski turned and motioned for Christina to stop. Beyond them, a maze of tracks crisscrossed their way through the yard, all leading to the train that Christina had spent so many nights dreaming about. Smoke poured from its stack, a white thick cloud boiling up to corrupt a black sky. Christina was sure that it was the most beautiful sight she had ever seen.

"This is the last chance you'll have to back out," Skiorski said without emotion.

"I'm going."

"It could get rough."

"I'm not afraid."

"You better be."

Christina reached in the pocket of her tattered coat and felt the cold metal of the small pistol Irena had given her. She had never fired one before.

She wondered about the single bullet.

Was it meant for someone else?

Or for her?

Could she even use the pistol if she needed it?

Doubt fogged her mind. For an instant, she almost gave the gun back to Skiorski, then decided against it. I can't shoot anybody, she told herself. But I may have to.

God, why couldn't life be simple and easy again?

Or had it ever been simple and easy?

Christina didn't know, not anymore. She breathed deeply and tried to chase the doubts from her mind.

Skiorski was talking.

"Once I leave you here," he said matter-of-factly, "you're on your own. I don't know you. I've never seen you before. If the Russians catch you, you belong to them, and may God have mercy on your soul. If I have to,

I'll even run you down myself and turn you over to them."

He paused, and his voice broke.

"I'm sorry, Christina," he apologized. "I really am. I hope you make it home all right and find everybody you're looking for. I pray that you will." He took her fragile hand in his and squeezed it. "I'll find a way to get you on the train. I promised you that much. But I can't fight for you. I won't fight for you. You've chosen to jeopardize your life, and I won't criticize you for that. But I won't jeopardize mine." He smiled sadly. "I just wanted you to understand."

Christina stood on her tiptoes and kissed him lightly on the cheek.

"Thank you," she whispered.

"Stay here and keep in the shadows," he told her, "and watch for my signal. When I wave my handkerchief, it's all right to come. Walk slowly and stay as far away from the lights as you can. There'll be other people milling around, but they'll all be too busy to pay you any attention. Just ignore them. Come straight to the baggage car. I'll leave the door cracked for you."

Skiorski patted her shoulder awkwardly, adjusted his cap, and strode boldly across the open yard, looking neither right nor left, simply walking as quickly as possible toward his waiting train.

Christina was shivering and couldn't understand why. The sedation had worn off hours ago, and the morning was warm and muggy. Yet she was freezing beneath the black, baggy coat that hung heavy around her shoulders, even though a clammy sweat plastered her face. She glanced down at the black oversize shoes on her feet, the black cotton stockings that hid her legs. There was dirt on her hands, and Irena had smudged her face with mud. Christina's face was pallid, devoid of any makeup, and there was a sincere touch of apprehension in her eyes.

At last, she thought, I'm going home.

My family's there.

My friends are waiting to see me.

And I'm ugly.

I've never looked this ugly in my whole life.

A sharp pain shot through her stomach, and Christina figured it was nerves or, perhaps, the acid from those stiff cups of black coffee. It felt as though she had drunk from a cauldron of hot grease.

She sat on her suitcase and watched the broad-shouldered figure of Skiorski growing smaller in the distance. Dawn, she guessed, was another hour away. Christina itched where the rough, course fabric of the dress touched her skin, and she felt a drop of sweat roll slowly down her back.

Time had deserted her, and weariness began to seep into her muscles. She ached. She wondered what had become of Skiorski. He was no longer visible, and the smoke was growing thicker as it rose hissing into the night. The train would no doubt be leaving soon.

Had he deserted her, too?

Then she saw it, the handkerchief, barely discernible in the dim light as Skiorski walked nonchalantly from around the engine, stopped momentarily to wipe his brow, then lifted it above his head as he yawned and stretched. To the casual eye, he was nothing more than a tired man who had probably stayed awake too late last night and had gotten up long before he was ready to. In that respect, he was no different from the rest of the crew, all of whom were sleepily going through the boredom, the drudgery of their regular morning routine.

The moment had finally arrived.

Christina wanted to laugh aloud as exhilaration flowed through her veins. Her anxiety had subsided, and she was no longer afraid. She gripped the leather handle of her suitcase tightly, straightened her shoulders, and marched confidently toward the train. If anyone had noticed her, he would have probably wondered what a poor, fragile, peasant woman had to grin about so early in the morning.

Christina slowed her pace, keeping herself in the clumsy shadows that the row of railroad cars cast across the yard. The train loomed closer, and the hissing of steam grew louder as the fire roared angrily in the boiler. Skiorski saw her coming and turned his back, stuffing his handkerchief into his coat pocket. At the moment, the tracks were deserted.

"Hey, Skiorski."

Christina's heart stopped at the sound of a human voice.

"Yeah."

"She's about as hot as she's gonna get."

The fireman looked down from the engine room, his aging face caught in the red glow of the blaze behind him, glazed with sweat, blackened by smoke.

Christina frantically looked around for a place to hide. There was none.

It was too late to run.

"Let's take her out of here, then," Skiorski yelled above the noise of the fire. He pulled himself up the steps and swung into the engine room.

"Maybe we can even get on back home early tonight," the fireman told him.

"Maybe."

Christina watched as both men disappeared from view. Over her left shoulder, she saw the crack in the doorway of the baggage car. She looked quickly up and down the track. No one was in sight. Christina wedged her suitcase through the narrow opening, then crawled in behind it, tearing a hole in her black cotton stockings as she tumbled into the musty interior of the car.

It was in total disarray, piled high with crates and cartons that had been carelessly thrown inside and hopelessly crammed together, and she slowly burrowed her way through the jumbled accumulation of boxes and made herself a hiding place in the darkness, curled up in a space barely wide enough for her to breathe. The dust was suffocating. It coated her arms and face, and her legs were twisted awkwardly beneath her. She held her suitcase in her lap, and the stained, rusting walls, ominous and barely visible, began to slowly close in around her.

The metal door slammed shut.

The train jerked forward, moving first at a snail's pace, then gradually picking up speed as it rumbled and creaked toward the outskirts of Berlin. The whistle blew long and mournful, and it reminded Christina of a funeral dirge. She shuddered. As the early patches of morning light seeped into the baggage car, she realized that she was leaning against a wooden coffin. It rattled as the train bounced roughly along the tracks, and a crate beside her threatened to topple over at any minute. She felt the pangs of loneliness, then sadness, then irritation, and finally Christina was gripped by a deep sense of helplessness. She was, it seemed, always at someone else's mercy: her aunt and uncle, the Russian major, the British commander, Dr. Joseph Smith, and now Skiorski. Thus far, she had been fortunate. When, she wondered, would her luck run out?

Christina closed her eyes and lay across the coffin as the train raced across the German countryside toward Poland. She drifted in and out of sleep, cramped, unable to shift her position amidst the boxes, and her muscles throbbed. The heat was stifling and the air around her stale and rancid from the smell of rotting vegetables. Christina removed her black scarf and wiped the sweat, streaked with mud, from her face. The vibration from the train reverberated through her small body, and a dull pain pounded the back of her head. She struggled to breathe in the oppressive heat and bowed her head but was too tired to pray.

Skiorski sat relaxed in the engine room, watching the early-morning haze spread gently across the land, reaching back into the dark shadows of the forest. To him, it had always been a special time of the day, a time of awakening, when the world was at peace with itself. He glanced at his watch. The train was two hours out of Berlin, and he knew that the most difficult part of Christina's escape was behind him. Skiorski smiled inwardly. He felt better than he had in days. In another hour or so, he would be pulling into the station at Slubice. Christina, without any trouble at all, could quickly lose herself in the crowd, and, for him, the ordeal would all be over.

Skiorski stared down the tracks with half-opened eyes. Boredom, he sometimes thought, was merely part of the job. He yawned, then stood and checked in the boiler room. The fire was raging brightly, and the train was moving along at a fast clip. He folded his arms and leaned against the window, letting the warm air brush against his face and ruffle his hair. Skiorski's nerves were settled now and he knew he should have taken time for breakfast. But he hadn't been hungry then, only a little frightened and cursing himself for being stupid enough to risk his own life to smuggle a complete stranger, no matter how pretty, out of Germany.

Soon, he would be crossing the Polish border.

Soon, he wouldn't have to worry anymore.

Soon, Christina would be out of his and Irena's lives.

Soon.

In another hour or so.

Skiorski rubbed his ruddy face and frowned. There was movement down alongside the track.

Four men.

He could barely make them out.

One was waving.

He was waving for the train to stop.

Why?

Here they were out in the middle of nowhere.

And some fool was waving for the train to stop.

Skiorski could see them better now.

All four were wearing Russian uniforms.

They were carrying submachine guns.

One swaggered onto the track, spread his legs, and fired defiantly into the air.

Skiorski didn't want a runaway train.

Skiorski didn't want to die.

He reached for the brakes, and the train groaned to a sudden stop, its wheels squealing and complaining as they slid amidst smoke and steam down the iron rails.

Christina was jarred awake.

Outside, she heard Skiorski asking, "What do you want?"

"We are going to search the train."

The words had a definite Russian accent, and Christina was numb with terror.

Did they know about her?

Were they looking for her?

The door to the baggage car was jerked open, and Christina found herself staring into the cold, black eyes of a Russian officer, standing not more than six feet away. He blinked, unaccustomed to the darkness that surrounded the interior of the car. Christina crouched low, not daring to breathe. The officer began shoving boxes aside, and Skiorski was at his side, his face twisted in scorn and anger.

"You have no right to stop this train," the engineer yelled indignantly.

The Russian pointed to the insignia on his collar. "This gives me all the authority I need," he said smugly.

"It's against the law."

"We make our own laws."

The Russian laughed and motioned for one of his men to climb into the baggage car.

"There's nothing of value in there," Skiorski told him, shrugging an apology. "The boxes are filled with parts for your factories. The luggage belongs to poor farmers and peasants who are trying to scratch out a living and doing a damn poor job of it. All they've got are a few ragged clothes, and you have no use for them. They couldn't even make a fire hot enough to warm your hands on a cold night, and the nights aren't even cold anymore."

The Russian officer frowned.

"Of course, there's a wooden coffin in there," Skiorski continued. "But, I'm afraid, none of you have any need for that. Not yet anyway." He grinned sardonically.

The officer spit in disgust.

"You'd be better off with a carton of cigarettes."

The Russian raised an eyebrow.

"And, maybe, a bottle of American whiskey."

The Russian scowled. "You are trying to bribe us." It was an accusation.

Skiorski shrugged and turned away. "You have a hard life," he said piously. "It's not pleasant being here in Germany when you had rather be home. Who knows? You may never get home again. You have to take the good times where you find them, and there's not many places to find them, I'm afraid. A few cigarettes . . . a little whiskey . . . it's the least I can do to help the soldiers who marched into Germany to liberate us."

"Where did you get them?"

"The black market in Berlin." Skiorski reached into his coat pocket and pulled out a crumpled pack of old cigarettes, offering one to the Russian. The officer grabbed the whole pack, stared at it for a moment, and quickly stuffed it into his jacket.

"Is this all you have?" he asked.

Skiorski shook his head. "I was carrying a carton of cigarettes and a bottle of American whiskey to a relative of mine in Poland," he answered. "He sometimes lets me trade them for some poultry and bacon. It's damn near impossible to find meat of any kind in Berlin these days."

"We kill a dog sometimes."

Skiorski nodded. "You do what you have to do."

"Where are these cigarettes and this American whiskey?" The Russian's animosity had cooled.

"You have your job, and I have mine." the engineer patiently explained. "And we have hell to pay if we don't do them right." He paused and glanced briefly into the baggage car where the Russian soldier stood poised and ready, waiting for the order to go through every box and every crate if necessary.

Christina was so close to him she could hear his breathing, smell the stench of his unwashed uniform. Her throat was dry, and she tightly gripped the small pistol, holding it close to her face.

There were four Russians.

She had one bullet.

She couldn't waste it.

At last she knew for sure who the one bullet was for.

"I have a schedule to keep," she heard Skiorski say, "and the company expects me to keep it. If you search the train, there's no way I can make it to Slubice on time. And I'll have to fill out endless forms, explaining the delay. It'll go bad for me. It could go worse for you, if the company files a complaint and finds you at fault."

The officer's eyes darkened with contempt. "Is that a threat?" he snapped caustically.

"No." Skiorski laughed. "I would never threaten you. You have the guns."

The Russian laughed with him.

Skiorski became serious again. "You take the cigarettes and the whiskey, and I'll be on my way. It's good for you." He shrugged. "It's good for me."

For a moment, the Russian officer fidgeted with his submachine gun, looking up and down the train. All he saw in the windows were ashen, sunken faces with hollow eyes staring back at him. The poor didn't interest him. Neither did their belongings. He glanced toward his men, and it struck him that their ashen, sunken faces, their hollow eyes were no different from the peasants on the train. Cigarettes, good ones, were virtually impossible to find anymore. And it had been such a long time since any of them had had the taste of rich whiskey on their tongues.

The officer turned to Skiorski, held out his hand, and snapped his fingers impatiently.

The engineer climbed into the train and returned seconds later with the cigarettes and whiskey. The Russian soldiers were beaming. They broke out in laughter, dropped their guns, and scrambled for the loose cigarettes that the officer threw at their feet. The young man jumped down from his perch inside the baggage car, and Skiorski quickly slammed the door shut and locked it. He and the baggage car had suddenly been forgotten. The soldiers had better things on their minds.

The train left them there, and the Russians officer turned away from the smoke that belched up from beneath the engine, walking slowly back down the track, drinking long and steady from the bottle he held with trembling hands.

Skiorski stared straight ahead, afraid to look back over his shoulder, expecting to hear a machine gun blast at any time and feel the bullets tearing into his back. Would they hurt? Or would he have time to feel anything at all? It was such a warm, sunny day to die.

Inside the baggage car, Christina sobbed with relief, and the tension finally ebbed out of her body. She felt the pistol slip out of her hand and heard it slide beneath the edge of the coffin. She made no attempt to retrieve it.

The bullet had been for her.

That frightened her.

She knew that, if necessary, she would have pulled the trigger without hesitation.

Christina lay face down on the coffin and envied the nameless one inside. Someone was beyond all pain, all fear, all suffering. She had not been able to outdistance hers, but she was still running, and she was so tired of running. Only death could stop her. She had been within seconds of stopping herself. It the soldier had found her, if he had touched her, she would be with the body in the coffin.

She lay there, too tired to move, too weak to struggle any longer, and waited patiently for the end to come, if it were time for the end to come, in Poland.

Less than an hour later, the train eased to a stop, and the door to the baggage car was again unlocked and left ajar. Sunlight threaded its way inside the compartment, and Christina propped herself up, squinting against the sudden burst of brightness, watching a strange array of faces file solemnly past the opening. They all looked so familiar to her, yet she knew she didn't know any of them. Still, they were her people, and they were speaking loudly and openly in the tongue of her homeland. It was like music, and her pulse was beating wildly as Christina slowly began to free herself from the cage of boxes and crates that had both hidden and entrapped her.

Her legs had lost their feeling, and she stumbled over the coffin, falling against the door. She rubbed her calves vigorously in an effort to stimulate the blood circulation again, and it seemed as though a thousand pins and needles were being thrust beneath her skin. Christina tied the black scarf back around her head, pulled her suitcase to the edge of the crack, and peered cautiously out the doorway.

The station platform was packed with people, some coming from the train, some running to board it, others pressing their way forward to wave goodbye. There were smiles. And kisses. And tears. Some of the strangers were in rags, some in uniform. A few had blank stares on their faces.

The whistle blew sharply.

Christina swallowed hard, held her breath, and slid to the ground, pulling the suitcase down after her. She glanced quickly, nervously, around. No one was watching. No one had seen her leave the train, no one who cared anyway. She turned with the flow of the crowd, kept her head bowed, and shuffled methodically toward the steps that led from the far end of the wooden platform.

Christina stopped.

Ahead, she saw the broad-shouldered figure of Skiorski, leaning against the engine. He checked his watch, keeping a close eye on the passengers boarding his train. Christina abruptly broke away from the crowd and moved toward him. He saw her coming, but looked past her. There were no signs of recognition at all on his face.

"Thank you," she whispered as she walked past him.

He ignored her.

But Christina thought she saw the faint glimmer of a satisfied smile playing about the corners of his mouth.

She didn't slow down, and her feet, after seven long years, finally touched Polish soil. She wanted to shout with happiness. She wanted to fall to her knees and kiss the good earth beneath her. She wanted to stop every stranger she met and say proudly, "I'm home. At last, I'm home."

Instead, she kept walking, afraid to smile, afraid to speak to anyone. The scarf blew off her head, and she let it go. The dress, sweated down, clung to her slender body, and she felt the black cotton stockings falling down around her ankles. Christina no longer cared. There was no reason to camouflage herself anymore. Besides, she had grown tired of being a peasant woman, a refugee, a displaced person on the run. Now she wanted to hold her head high and be the person God had meant for her to be. She stepped into the terminal and hurried straight to the ladies bathroom, eager to become Christina Skiba again.

She washed the dirt from her hands, the mud stains from her face, then removed the black dress and cotton stockings, carefully folding them and laying them in the corner of the empty room. She wouldn't need them any-more. Maybe someone else would. From her suitcase, she took a pink blouse, navy blue suit, and pair of Italian shoes. She ripped open the lining in her tattered coat and quickly transferred her money, documents, and jew-elry to a matching purse. After being gone seven years, her mother and father might not recognize her, but they would be proud of her. Christina was making sure of it. She was throwing all caution to the wind and going home in style. She paused a moment before the mirror and ran a comb through the tangles in her hair, then added a touch of rouge to her cheeks.

Christina smiled, then laughed out loud. She winked at herself, picked up her suitcase, and walked back out into the terminal humming an old Polish song she hadn't thought of in years. She had learned it as a child. It had become the song of her homecoming. But for the life of her, Christina couldn't remember the words.

She purchased a one-way ticket to Bydgoszcz from a dour little man who looked at her stylish clothes with disfavor and simply grunted when she spoke to him. His attitude startled her, but this was one day she wasn't going to let anybody ruin. Even the Russians with sub-machine guns had failed. The potato soup in the cafe was too cold, but Christina didn't mind. She barely tasted it anyway, watching the people pass by, laughing as though nothing had changed, as though nothing had been spoiled by a war that erupted on Polish soil. She didn't have to envy them now or ever again. She was one of them, just another Polish passenger quietly biding her time and waiting for the first afternoon train heading east.

For once, it was on time.

By the time the train reached the station at Bydgoszcz, the sun had fallen behind the factory smokestacks, and the buildings downtown, derelicts scarred by the bombs of war, were casting long, ominous shadows across the streets.

Christina bounded down the steps and looked around. The warm glow that had enveloped her earlier in Slubice was abruptly replaced by a chill she could not explain. The waiting was over. The anguish had ended.

She was home.

Then why did she feel so uneasy?

The courtyard in front of the railway station looked as it always had, neatly manicured and ablaze with the stunning colors of roses and gladiolas, cornflowers and sunflowers. The streetcars were still there, fighting with automobiles for position as they came grinding around the square. That was familiar, too. Christina couldn't imagine Bydgoszcz without its streetcars. She had forgotten them, and she was so glad to see them again. Little ragged urchins with smiling faces, probably no more than ten years old, were running toward her, all eager to carry her suitcase to a nearby taxi for a price. Most of the businessmen in town had earned their first coins that way.

She tried to smile.

Nothing had changed.

Christina's nerves were raw and on edge. Fatigue had set in, and she shivered for no accountable reason. She felt sick, as though someone had kicked her in the stomach, and there was the unmistakable smell of death in her nostrils.

She paid a brown-eyed, rusty-faced urchin five *zlotys* to carry her suitcase to the taxi and got in the back seat.

"Where to?"

She gave the driver the address of her father's home.

He looked at her strangely, then shrugged and nodded. Christina couldn't take her eyes off him. He wasn't much older than she was, and his face had been badly burned. The skin graft was red and swollen, and it had left his mouth in a perpetual sneer.

Through his rearview mirror, the driver saw her staring at him. "It was the war," he explained, his voice cool and detached. "A plane went down on our street and threw burning shrapnel all over us." His grin was half-cocked. "I don't guess I'm as pretty as I used to be."

Embarrassed, Christina looked away.

"I'm sorry," she said softly.

"It's not your fault." He laughed. "And, I didn't expect you to kiss me." His laughter had turned bitter.

Christina reddened. She wished she were somewhere else. She wished she had taken another cab. She wished he hadn't seen her staring at him that way.

"How bad was it?" she asked.

"What?"

"The war."

"It got us all," he said without emotion, "some worse than others. But there didn't nobody escape it, man, woman, nor child."

The taxi turned the corner, and Christina suddenly knew where she was. It was all so familiar, the houses, the street where she had run as a child, the sidewalk where she and her friends had skipped rope and played dolls and tattled when someone was bad, and someone was always bad. It was as though she had never left at all.

But something was wrong.

Dreadfully wrong.

"Here's where you wanted to go, lady," the driver said.

Christina, as if in slow motion, crawled out of the taxi and gazed upon the neighborhood of her youth. This was the moment she had dreamed about and prayed for, the moment that she doubted would ever come.

Now it had.

Home. She was really home.

Her father would be so surprised, but he wouldn't let it show. He never did. Her mother would cry and hug her neck and carry on something awful about how pretty she was and how much of a young lady Christina had become. Mothers were like that, especially hers. And they would sit up all night, laughing and talking and trying hard to catch up on the seven long years that had kept them apart and passed them by.

But something was wrong.

Christina walked to her father's house and stared with disbelieving eyes. It wasn't there anymore. All she saw was a burned-out shell that reeked with the smell of death. The last thing she heard before the world turned black was the scream that came from her own throat.

Chapter 12

CHRISTINA WAS SITTING ON THE EDGE of the curb, her head leaning against the taxi driver's shoulder when she opened her eyes. It was as though she were looking through a blue haze, and everything around her was distorted and slightly out of sync. Her head throbbed, and her arms hurt where she had scratched them against the cement when she fell. Blood had smudged the sleeve of her pink blouse. Christina's breath was coming in short, painful bursts, and, at the moment, she felt detached, as if she were a stranger, an intruder in a place that no longer belonged to her.

"What's the matter with you, lady?" the driver asked as he helped Christina to her feet.

"The house." She pointed to the hollow, crumbling shell before her, and even her voice sounded unfamiliar. "It's my house. My mother and father live there. They've lived there all my life. What happened to it?"

The driver shrugged and a crooked grin appeared on his disfigured face. "Lady," he said bluntly, "you must have been away from here for a long time."

"Seven years."

He grunted. "Bydgoszcz died."

"It looks the same."

"It's not the same." The driver dusted off his cap and leaned back against his taxi, "It won't ever be the same again. Like I told you, lady, the war touched everybody, some of us worse than others."

He held out his hand.

Christina rummaged through her purse, pulled out a half dozen coins and paid him.

"Where you going to go now?" he asked.

Christina didn't answer him. She began walking down the broken sidewalk as if in a trance, her eyes staring straight ahead, seeing everything and seeing nothing, and by the time she reached the corner, Christina was in a dead run.

War did change people's lives, she told herself, as she raced out of breath toward the center of town. It took away what they had. Their dreams were crushed everytime a bomb fell and everytime a house erupted into flames, forcing someone new out into the street. Christina understood. She had seen it during the seige of Budapest. She had heard their wails of anguish, watched as families huddled together, their faces frozen in horror as those burning embers danced in the night sky above their heads. She had wept with them, then never saw them again as they fled to any shelter they could find. But people adjusted. Her mother would. People were strong. And none were stronger than her father. He would keep the family together, no matter what the Germans had done to drive them apart. He had steel in his spine. He was a survivor.

Christina followed a pathway where she had run so many times before, and, for a moment, she was a child again on her way to her grandmother's house. The flowers were in bloom, and they climbed along the back fences, filling the air with the sweet fragrance of summer. A skittish alley cat bolted across the street, snarling his displeasure at being awakened so rudely on a hot afternoon. In the distance, amidst the harsh noise of the traffic, Christina heard the clanging of streetcar bells and knew she was near, almost there.

She rounded a corner.

And held her breath.

There it was!

The taxi driver had been wrong, and Christina felt like crying for joy. The war hadn't touched everybody.

Her grandmother's house stood tall and strong just as it had for ages. It looked exactly the way Christina remembered, an old, gray, three-story brick with flower boxes, overburdened with blooms, decorating the upper floor balconies. The walls had only been slightly damaged. Perhaps it was stray gunfire that had chipped away at the facade. Other buildings had suffered. her own home lay in ruins. But her grandmother's house had withstood the Nazi *Blitzkrieg*, a fortress, a refuge to shelter and protect her family during the darkest days of the war.

Breathlessly, Christina bounded up the steps that led to the front door. White lace curtains framed the glass in the doorway, just like always.

She impatiently rang the bell and heard the faint sound of footsteps shuffling slowly down the hallway. In her mind, Christina pictured her grandmother the way she looked on that last, fateful morning in Bydgoszcz, standing in a navy blue dress on the platform of the railway station, waving goodbye and blowing kisses toward the departing train.

Christina had leaned far out the window and yelled, "I love you, Babcha."

She always wondered if her grandmother had heard her.

The footsteps were closer now.

How much had her Babcha changed? To Christina, she had always seemed old, jolly, and wrinkled with hair that was so white it was almost silver. The wrinkles would be deeper now, and her blue eyes had probably faded, their sparkle dimmed. After all, they had seen so much.

The door opened.

She was looking at the kindly face of an elderly woman with deep-set wrinkles, silver hair, and blue eyes that had faded and lost their sparkle.

She was staring into the eyes of a stranger.

Christina had yelled, "Grandmother, here I am."

The woman stepped back in astonishment.

"Hello," she said weakly, "can I help you?"

"Who are you," Christina blurted out without thinking. "Where is my grandmother? She lives here. This is her house. What are you doing here?"

"I live here now." The woman's voice was soft, and confusion clouded her eyes.

"Where is my grandmother?" Christina's high-pitched voice was tinged with hysteria.

"I don't know."

"She owns this house," Christina snapped.

"The government owns it now."

Christina felt the blood surge to her head. She wanted to pound her fist against the door and scream. My God, where was everybody. It was as though she were a stranger in her own hometown. Her family was gone. Everyone had vanished and left no trace. All she had were names, but they didn't belong to anybody anymore. Her eyes blurred, and she went cold, slowly dying inside, feeling like she had when she was three years old and her mother and father drove away for a weekend holiday that

August morning. It was the first time Christina had ever been separated from them overnight. She had crawled into the closet and buried her face in a pillow, too frightened to cry, believing that she would never see them again. But she had had her grandmother then.

Now there was no one.

They were all gone, displaced persons as she had been, chased from their own homes, their lives shattered, and maybe it was too late for anyone to pick up the broken pieces again.

Christina would try.

But only if she could find them.

She felt the old woman gently touch her arm. "Why don't you come in," she said slowly as the door widened. "I don't know if I can help you, but I'll do my best."

Inside, the rooms were sparsely furnished, but clean and well kept. Christina recognized the blue wallpaper on the dining room wall, the wood-fired hot water heater in the bathroom. It made her feel good to see them again. There was the kitchen table where she had eaten breakfast on so many summer mornings, the rug worn threadbare by her grandmother's feet. Christina had danced upon it as a child while her Babcha sang, and when she closed her eyes she could almost hear the song again, and she hummed it quietly to herself.

Christina, chasing forgotten memories as she had once chased after butterflies down the back streets of Bydgoszcz, followed the old woman from room to room, listening as she talked.

She had fled the fighting in her own hometown and come to the gray, three-story brick house in 1945. It was deserted then, nothing but bare rooms and bare walls. A few pieces of dusty furniture had been thrown into the basement, and she salvaged what she could to start life anew. She had heard that the Polish family who formerly lived there suddenly left in a big hurry sometime during the German occupation of 1944. No one remembered them. No one remembered why. At least no one wanted to talk about it. A Nazi SS officer had moved in with his wife and child for a time, but he, too, left in a big hurry when the Russian troops finally fought their way into the outskirts of Bydgoszcz. Hitler had sent butchers. The Russians were almost as brutal.

That's all she knew, the old woman said.

She was sorry.

She left Christina standing alone in an empty room of the big house, immersed in her own thoughts and fears.

The gilded mirror with the marble base. Where was it? And the grandfather clock, the china cabinet, the crystal bowls that once set so proudly upon the table. The painting of the Lord's Last Supper should be on the wall, and the family's most prized possession, the reproduction of Rubens's *Madonna and Child*, was missing from the other.

Like her grandmother, they were gone.

Thrown away.

Lost.

Or, most likely, stolen.

And no one remembered why. That's what the old woman had said. Those who knew refused to talk about it. Some memories become nightmares.

Some nightmares don't end.

Christina wearily walked back out into the early evening shadows and stopped the first empty taxicab that she saw being driven her way.

"The Utza Dolina," she told the driver, her voice flat and drained of emotion.

"Got an address?"

She gave him one.

It was her last chance to find her family, and she knew it. Christina was facing the reality that she had avoided for so long. When her mother's letters stopped coming, she had blamed it on the Germans, then the Russians. The borders to Poland had been closed, and no mail got out or got in. That's what Christina told herself, and that's what she believed. Not once had she let herself even consider the fact that her mother and father, her grandmother, might have been forced to leave Bydgoszcz. It had been so easy thinking that they were still living in sheltered comfort, as always, waiting for her and untouched by the war that had raged across Europe.

Christina slipped out of the taxi and paid her fare. Across the street, she saw the sign that she had hoped for, the one hanging above her Aunt Sophie's small grocery store, the Colonialka, its painted letters worn and faded by too many years of neglect. She had gone there so often as a child, and her Uncle Kostek would slip her sticks of hard candy when no one was looking, and she would sit and listen for hours while her mother and Sophie sat together in front of the fireplace, trading recipes and gossip, sometimes whispering to keep her innocent ears from hearing the truth about people she didn't know anyway. The letters weren't worn and faded then. Christina felt a sense of hope rising within her. Or was it merely desperation?

In the fading light of dusk, she saw a lamp burning brightly in the store.

Someone was home.

Was it Aunt Sophie?

Christina waited for a streetcar to pass by. She had a mad urge to run across the street, but she hesitated, walking stiffly, mechanically, toward the Colonialka, afraid to open the door, afraid of who she might or might not find inside. Through the window, Christina glimpsed a woman behind the counter, her blonde hair threaded with patches of gray, deep lines cut sharply into a face that had aged far beyond its years. She was a tall woman with haunted eyes and slumping shoulders. To Christina, she was frightening, but beautiful.

The young girl burst frantically through the doorway. "Hello, everybody," she shouted. "I'm home."

A customer whirled around with astonishment on his face. The woman behind the counter stared at the stranger who stood before her, dressed so stylishly in a war-stricken town where no one dressed stylishly anymore. The navy blue suit was creased with wrinkles, but it was perfectly tailored to fit the pretty young girl. The shoes must have been imported from Italy, and she was even carrying a matching handbag. The pink blouse had probably never been worn before. It still smelled new. Sophie turned cold. The face was so familiar, yet so young. Had Elizabeth come back? No, it couldn't be Elizabeth. Then a warm glow sank into her eyes, and a smile replaced the frown, and her hands began to visibly tremble.

"Christina." Her words were barely audible, even in the silence of the store. "Is that you?"

"Hello, Aunt Sophie."

The aging woman gathered her niece in her arms as tears blurred her eyes, holding the girl tightly, and whispering softly, "Our Krishchia has finally come back to us."

Christina's heart was pounding.

She saw Uncle Kostek follow his customer to the front door and lock it behind him. He gently hung a CLOSED sign in the window, standing there with troubled eyes, watching as the last shadows of daylight played upon the ground outside. The energy that once surged through his big, rawboned frame had disappeared. The laughter had died with it. Kostek had always been so strong, so sturdy, and now he was merely a hollow shell with sagging shoulders and a pallid face. He had not yet spoken to the little girl who, so many times in the past, had talked him out of sweet stick candy.

Christina's distraught eyes searched the room for other faces she knew should be there, faces that she expected to be in the store with Sophie.

There were none.

She listened for other voices.

She heard none.

She broke away from Sophie's grasp and screamed, "Where are they?"

Silence.

Sophie turned her head, her long fingers digging into Christina's arms until they hurt.

"Where's mama?"

Kostek's shoulders stiffened.

"And papa?"

Sophie crumpled into a chair, no longer able to look Christina in the eyes. Her face twitched uncontrollably, and Kostek leaned against the front doorway, hiding his face with his hands.

"And Babcha?" Her voice softened, and Christina barely recognized it as her own.

The dread that had been buried deep inside her began to tear loose and surface. Christina glanced from Sophie to Kostek, and she knew that her mother and father, her grandmother, were gone now and would not be coming back. The anguish on their faces told her everything she wanted to know and everything she was afraid to hear.

Christina stumbled backward.

"They are dead, aren't they?" she said.

For too long now, Sophie had kept her grief bottled up within her. She had confronted life one day at a time, always looking steadfastly toward tomorrow, never daring to let the past and its tragedies catch up with her. She hadn't run from reality. She had merely blotted it out of her mind. The war had dropped a final curtain around her, separating the old from the new, the bad from the good, death from life. It had not been easy to accept. Sophie had made herself forget. It was the only way she could retain her sanity in a world that had become insane.

The cry was at first a low moan, coming from the depths of a soul that had found no peace, the guttural sound of a woman dying, the anguish of a woman who had fallen into a living hell and could not die. It haunted the room and chilled everyone it touched. The screams came before the tears, and the tears cleansed the heart but not the soul.

Sophie pounded the chair until her fists were raw and bleeding.

Her body shook as though it were wracked with fever. Her eyes were opaque, her face shrunken and bloodless, her veins blue and protruding from beneath the thin, waxen skin that stretched across her temples. The crying stopped long before the screams faded into the silence of a Polish night.

Christina paced the floor.

Kostek had poured them both a cup of coffee, then knelt beside his wife and held her close to him, gently stroking her hair, whispering quietly to comfort her until she had stopped shaking.

"What happened to my parents?" Christina asked her uncle.

He ignored her.

"I have a right to know."

"Sophie will tell you."

"Sophie has suffered enough."

Kostek turned and stared at Christina, coldly remote, intent on keeping his secrets to himself. "The pain has only begun," he said. "It cuts deep. It festers. It poisons. No matter how hard you try to make it go away, it's always there. I know. I watch Sophie die a little each day, and I die a little with her."

"And my parents?"

"What you need to know, Sophie will tell you."

Christina looked down at her aunt. She looked so old, so helpless, so frightened. There was a hint of horror embedded deep within her eyes. Christina could only guess what the woman knew, what she had seen. She remembered her own home lying in a pile of rubble, destroyed by the German bombs that had rained violently down upon Poland. Bydgoszcz had not escaped Hitler's wrath. Neither had her mama, her papa, her babcha. Had death come to them quickly, she wondered. Or did they suffer as the flames leaped up around them? Had they even seen the bomb that tore through their home?

It must have been in 1941, Christina decided. That's why the letters stopped coming.

That's when the end had come.

She rubbed her eyes, and a strange feeling of relief swept over Christina. The years of waiting and hoping were behind her. Now she knew what had happened to them all.

It hurt.

But at least she knew, and she no longer had to keep lying to herself, and Christina could accept the truth.

Her aunt's breath was coming in short gasps. Sophie swallowed hot black coffee to calm her nerves, and Kostek wiped the tear stains from the wrinkles in her face. The sobbing had subsided, and gradually the color was returning to her cheeks.

"I'm sorry, Krischa," she said hoarsely.

She reached out with a cold, trembling hand and touched Christina's face, caressing it as she had done so many times before when the young woman beside her was a child.

"I thought you were dead, too."

"I know." Christina took the old woman's hand and squeezed it affectionately.

"Everyone is dead."

Christina fought back a tear. "Are they all buried together in the family plot?" she asked. "That's the way they would have wanted it."

Silence.

Sophie began to shake again, and her voice broke. "I don't know where they are buried," she said.

Christina went rigid.

"What do you mean?"

Sophie opened her mouth to speak, but no words came out. Her lips quivered.

Christina felt a cold rush of wind pass through the room.

"They just went away one day," Sophie said, her lips barely moving. "They just went away and never came back."

Christina's palms were sweating, and her throat went dry. Was there no end to this madness? Or had the nightmare just begun? Fear settled down around her shoulders, and she found it difficult to breathe or even comprehend the words she was hearing. They didn't make sense. Her worst fears had been realized, but still Christina didn't fully understand the muted traces of horror that she saw reflected in her aunt's eyes. The sweat on her forehead became cold and clammy, and suddenly she did not want to know what had happened to her family, and she silently cursed herself for even returning to Bydgoszc. In ignorance, there had been hope. In Budapest, even in Berlin, she had slept well at night believing that her family was safe within the sanctity of their hometown, struggling, perhaps, unhappy, no doubt, but safe. The war had merely separated them for awhile. That was all. In time they would be back together again, and time would heal their wounds and repair the years that had been stolen from them. Now Christina knew she must face the hard reality that had tortured her aunt and turned her into an old woman before her fiftieth year.

Sophie stared at Christina, but no longer saw her. She had regained her composure now and was searching the darkened recesses of her mind for the tragic memories that had been locked away there but never quite forgotten.

"Your father was the first to go," she said quietly.

He had been quickly called to service as an officer in the medical corps shortly after the Nazis stormed across the border. There was much bleeding and dying. Pavel had been a pharmacist. He knew how to treat the bleeding and the dying.

In the forest near Katowice, he and forty-one other Polish officers had been surrounded and captured by a German patrol. They were rounded up and herded like animals deep into the woodland thickets.

An SS officer had lined them up.

He checked their credentials.

He apologized for the war.

As he walked away, his storm troopers shot them all to death, one at a time, and the officer laughed as each man flinched at the sound of gunfire and waited for his turn to die.

It took so long.

It happened so fast.

The war was barely two weeks old.

Christina felt a sense of panic, then pity, rising within her. Her mother had known, God bless her. She had gotten the word quickly, Sophie said, but Pavel's body had never been brought out of the forest. He just left one day and marched off to war, and she never saw him again, dead or alive. All those times she sat down to write her daughter in Budapest, she had known. But not once had she ever left even a hint in her letters that something terrible had happened. She knew. But Christina must not know about her father. Elizabeth Skiba chose to spare her daughter any sorrow and bear her burden of grief alone.

"The war was difficult for us all," Sophie continued. "The Poles and the Jews suffered unbearably. I don't know why Hitler wanted to make life so miserable for the Poles and the Jews, but he did. At times, it seemed we were only one meal away from starvation.

"But we held on. And our faith kept us together no matter how bad it got."

She paused as her voice weakened.

"The Germans stripped away our pride, then our dignity," Sophie said softly. "They wanted to terminate our heritage. Finally the Germans handed down an edict that prohibited anyone from speaking Polish on the street. We even whispered in our homes. There were ears everywhere, listening, waiting for someone to make a mistake.

"You only made one."

Sophie rose and shuffled toward the front window, a sad, wistful look on her face.

"It was on a Sunday morning in March of 1941," she said. "Your mother, grandmother, and Aunt Jadwega had gone to early mass at St. Elizabeth Church. As they were walking home, a Gestapo agent heard them speaking to each other in Polish. He arrested them on the spot." Sophie shrugged as though she still couldn't believe what had happened. "That was their only crime," she suddenly shouted, her voice tired, yet hard as flint. "They were speaking Polish aloud in the street." Sophie turned and threw up her arms in frustration. "Is that so wrong? Is that such a horrid crime that it costs you your life?"

Christina felt flushed, anger slowly replacing the fear that had gnawed at her for so long.

Sophie leaned against the doorway and folded her arms, shivering even though the night was warm and muggy. "They were allowed to stop by their home long enough to pick up a few belongings," she said, "then they were taken down to the Gestapo headquarters and jailed.

"Your mother was permitted to write me a brief letter explaining their arrest, and I went down the next morning and asked for permission to see them. It was denied. I couldn't even see my own mother."

The tears came again.

"The Germans didn't care about me. The Germans didn't care about them. As far as they were concerned, we were all animals being led to a slaughter. And they butchered us without a conscience. I was told to come back a week later."

Sophie paused and wiped her eyes on the worn cotton sleeve of her dress.

"The Gestapo padlocked the door to your grandmother's house and nailed a sign on the wall forbidding anyone to enter it. The Germans had taken over. They wanted everything. They took everything. All that we owned now belonged to them, even our lives.

"I went back to the jail a week later. But my mother, Elizabeth and Jadwega were no longer there.

"They had been transferred to a work camp."

Six weeks later, just before daybreak one morning, Sophie was awakened by a smiling German soldier who apologized for knocking on her door so early in the day. He asked her to come to the Gestapo headquarters without delay, and she threw back her head and laughed aloud for the first time since her mother and sisters has been carried away. Surely, she told herself, the Germans had finally realized that it was all a mistake, just a simple misunderstanding. And her mother, Elizabeth, and Jadwega were all at the station house now, waiting on her to come and take them back home again. Maybe, there were Germans who were human after all.

Sophie walked in and stared into the cold, calloused face of the Gestapo agent. He glanced up from his papers, and she introduced herself. He frowned as though he preferred not be disturbed about trivial things, and his black eyes narrowed scornfully.

The agent spoke not a word.

He simply picked up a dirty little bundle of ragged clothes from the floor and pitched them to her.

"What are these?" Sophie asked, suddenly confused.

"They belonged to your relatives, I believe," he replied with boredom in his voice.

"Where's my mother?" Sophie's words were frantic.

"She's dead."

"And my sisters?"

"Dead."

"What happened to them?"

"Dysentery," he snapped.

Christina felt ill. She sat, unable to move, and watched her Aunt Sophie retrieve a small, pitiful bundle of clothes from her china cabinet, then place them in her lap.

"That's all we have left," the old woman said quietly. "They walked away to mass one morning and never came back, and that's all we have left to prove they ever lived at all."

Christina picked up a dress that she knew had belonged to her mother and carefully pressed out the folded wrinkles with her hand. It was so dirty it was a disgrace. Her mother had never worn dirty clothes in her life. It was so tattered. Christina couldn't even picture her mother with the dress on.

She held it lovingly to her face and asked, "Where was the work camp where she died?"

"In Poland."

"At least she died on Polish soil."

Sophie nodded.

"Was she buried there"

"I don't know. No one would ever tell me."

"What was the work camp called?"

Sophie took a deep breath and looked away.

"Auschwitz," she said.

And Christina screamed.

Silence.

She screamed again.

In her mind, she saw stark flashes of Auschwitz, black and white, and grainy.

Naked men and women, skeletons who had not yet died, trodding upon a frozen ground, their eyes hollow, their faces gaunt, their children running at their feet and crying out.

A hell without hope, where the spirit died long before the soul.

In silence.

They marched onward, the nameless, the unmourned, to the firing squads, to the gas chambers, to the crematoriums that were ablaze with their ashes.

Old faces.

Young faces.

Worn out faces.

Jewish faces.

Christina screamed again. My God, she thought, and among them were Polish faces.

My aunts.

My mother.

She screamed a last time.

And Kostek slapped her, then gently held her in his arms as he had during the days when they laughed together and shared his stolen sticks of candy.

Aunt Sophie was on the floor at her feet, weeping.

Christina felt herself die a little, and she no longer fought it. In the grave, here was no pain, no memories, no war, no Auschwitz, no family.

But that was all right, she told herself.

She didn't have a family anyway. It just walked away one day and never came back.

She smiled inwardly.

Without a word, Christina slipped into one of her aunt's bedrooms back behind the store, sat down, propped herself against the window and waited. For two days and two nights, she did not eat. She did not sleep. She simply waited to die and wondered why it took so long. There was a sting of disappointment each time she saw the rising of the sun.

On the third day, Christina decided she wasn't going to die, no matter how hard she tried, and she came out of the room. Sophie smiled. Christina looked past her. Kostek offered her a plate of food. She passed him by.

She walked alone in the garden, her mind full of questions that had no answers. Did her mother suffer? Had the bullets taken her father quickly? Was there pain? Was there time to pray? Why had she survived? Why had she even bothered to come back home?

Life for Christina had always been full of meaning.

Now the meaning was gone.

Her hopes were crushed beneath the hobnailed boots of the German blitz.

She must have had dreams. Surely, she did. Everyone dreamed dreams, but she could no longer remember what they were. She no longer cared what they were.

A doctor came at Sophie's urging to help her cope with the shock that was slowly destroying her.

Christina refused to see him.

Father Joseph Matuszak, the parish priest, sat in the garden with her. He was in his late forties, a small, slender man, about four inches shy of being six feet tall. He shared Christina's pain, her sense of loss. He had felt it before. During the war years, Father Matuszak had lost so many of his friends. He had preached so many funerals. There were so many familiar faces that would just suddenly turn up missing, and he never heard their names spoken again. With each new Sunday, he found more empty pews in the church, and he, too, sank to his knees and asked questions that had no answers.

Father Matuszak held Christina's hand and listened to the agony of her grief as they strolled together across the town square and into a park. The summer day smelled as fresh, as sweet as the flowers that grew in great, colorful banks down the terraced hillside.

He pointed to a small brown bird that sat chirping beside the black marble base of a fountain that symbolized the joy of freedom. To Christina, the fountain was a lie, a mockery. There was no joy, no freedom, for her or for anyone.

"Look at the little bird," Father Matuszak said softly.

"She has no place to go. She has no home. She has no one to care whether she lives or she dies."

The priest smiled sadly and squeezed her hand. "She's a lot like you, Christina. Yet listen how happy she is. Listen to her singing. No matter how terrible things may seem, no matter how unfair life becomes, she knows that someday she'll find a nest of her own. Then she will be home.

"So will you, Christina."

Christina broke her silence. "Why did my mama and my papa have to die?" she asked.

"God had a place for them."

"And why am I alive?"

"God must have a special plan for you."

Christina's eyes widened, touched by a new ray of hope. "When will I know what it is?" she asked.

"When the time comes, God will let you know."

Three weeks later, Aunt Sophie awakened Christina early. "You have a telegram," she said, a quizzical frown etched in the wrinkles of her face. "From a John Christy."

Christina's heart skipped a beat. She wasn't sure she had heard her aunt correctly. Perhaps she had merely been dreaming. She had been in a fog for days anyway.

"From who?" she asked sleepily.

"A John Christy."

Christina was out of the bed in a flash, taking the telegram from her aunt with trembling hands and hurriedly scanning it. John's ship, the *S.S. Robert W. Hurt*, would be docking in Gdansk, Poland, on July 7, it said. Would it be possible for her to meet him there? If not, could she call and leave word with the American Consul in Sopot?

John wanted to see her again. John had found her. Christina remembered again that before leaving Berlin, she had written him one last time and included the names and addresses of her mother, her grandmother, and Aunt Sophie. She expected him to throw the letter away. She never expected him to come looking for her, especially not on Polish soil.

"You're smiling," Sophie said, her face brightening. "It has been a long time since I've seen you smile."

"I'm going to Gdansk," Christina announced.

"Why?"

"John's ship is arriving there in two days, and he wants me to meet him."

Sophie frowned. "Who is John Christy?"

"He's in the Merchant Marines. I met him in Trieste when Aunt Vera, Uncle Arpad and I were there on a holiday last February."

Sophie folded her arms. "I will not allow you to run all over the country to meet a sailor," she snapped. "I will not have anyone thinking that my niece is a whore."

"He's not just a sailor," Christina snapped back. "He's the officer of the ship."

"I don't care if he's the captain." Sophie was adamant.

The spark had returned to Christina's eyes. Her face was flushed. "I'm nineteen years old," she argued.

"I don't care if you're thirty." Sophie began pacing the floor. "As long as you are single and living here with me and Kostek, you will not be allowed to go off and rendezvous with some strange man who I don't know and have never seen. Your mother wouldn't approve of it, and neither will I." She took the telegram from Christina and read it herself. "If this John Christy wants to see you so bad, then he can come here."

"That's absurd."

"Why?"

"He doesn't speak Polish and the seacoast is three hundred miles away from Bydgoszcz."

Christina could tell by the stern look on her Aunt Sophie's face that there was no reason to argue anymore.

The answer was no and it would always be no.

Christina might be nineteen. She had come halfway

across Europe alone, had worked in a Berlin medical clinic, had even been smuggled under Russian eyes into Poland. But that wasn't enough. In her aunt's eyes, she was still just a little girl and would always be a little girl, and there was nothing she could do about it.

Sophie's voice softened. "Call the consul," she said. "That's what John wanted you do. You owe him that much."

The phone rang only twice before it was answered.

"I want to speak to the American counsul," Christina said.

"Is it business?"

"It's urgent."

"Please wait."

The silence was broken only by the static in the line. Then Christina heard the gravel voice of the consul.

"Harold Green here," he said.

Christina patiently explained why she would not be able to meet John's ship, and shyly asked if he would relay the message to John. The young officer would simply have to come to Bydgoszcz if he expected to see her. Green laughed with genuine amusement at her predicament.

"Your request is a little irregular," he said, "I've never been asked to intrude in Cupid's territory before, but I'll do what I can for you. I'll make sure John Christy knows why you're not here. From then on, however, I'm afraid you and he are on your own." He laughed again, louder this time.

"Thank you," Christina said. It was barely a whisper.

"It's been a long war," Green replied. "It's about time somebody around here got a few lucky breaks. Maybe one of them will yours."

Christina started to hang up, but she heard the consul's voice again, "Young lady . . ."

"Yes?"

"Let me know how it turns out."

She hung up the phone and a feeling of helplessness overwhelmed her. Her heart was both heavy and saddened. She knew how it would turn out.

John would only have a day or two at the most in Gdansk, then he would be at sea again. He might want to come to Bydgoszcz. For some silly reason, he might have even missed her. They did have such a good time, but such a short time, together in Italy. But Bydgoszcz was simply too far away. He wouldn't be able to get there. He wouldn't have the time. John never had much time. The sea took it all.

This time, he would not have a girl in port.

Christina scolded herself for even getting so excited about hearing from him again. That had been foolish, and she felt foolish. She would probably never see John Christy again. It was that simple.

Chapter 13

THE TRAIN GROUND ITS WAY SLOWLY into Bydgoszcz, and its varied assortment of passengers began departing before the cars even came to a complete stop. Christina stood amidst the chaos and the noise of the railway station, frantically searching for one special face in the crowd that she knew was frantically searching for her. She elbowed her way through the soldiers and heard their whistles. Christina wasn't interested. They were a long way from home. She had no home, and the bitterness still ached in her heart. An old man, his hair long and white, carried a small grandson on his back. The boy was laughing. The boy had no legs. The bombs that took them had no conscience. A young girl was selling roses. Another was selling herself, and none of the soldiers wanted roses. Farmers were looking for their families. Families were looking for their sons. One had come home in a casket.

The faces all looked the same. Some were older. Some were smiling. Some were clean shaven. A few had beards. All had the same haunted eyes that had seen death, too much death, and their innocence had been lost in the battles and the brothels of someone else's war.

Christina felt a hand gently touch her arm. She whirled around and stared into the black, foreboding eyes of a Gypsy woman who had slithered through the crowd. She had dark olive skin and wore a twisted grin. Bracelets jangled together on her arm, and a flowered scarf fell around her shoulders.

She pulled a deck of worn, dirty cards from the pocket of her striped skirt and slowly began to shuffle them.

"I will tell your fortune," the Gypsy woman purred.

Christina shook her head.

"You have had much sadness in your life."

Christina tried to ignore her. She pushed forward, but the Gypsy woman grabbed her arm and stopped her. The twisted grin became a scowl.

"You can't run from your past," she said softly. "And neither can you run from your future."

Christina jerked loose. "I'm sorry," she said. "I don't have time for you."

The twisted grin returned. "Someday you will," the Gypsy woman murmured. "Someday you will want to know." She bowed her head and was swallowed up by the unruly throng of people who kept fighting their way across the platform, shouting and cursing at everyone and at no one in particular.

Christina turned, and she saw him, straining against the flow of the crowd, shoving his way toward her. She could not believe that John Christy was actually there until he put his arms around her and held her tightly. It was as though he had never been gone at all, and for a fleeting, foolish moment, Christina hoped he would never leave again. She buried her face against his chest and closed her eyes.

Today.

That's all she had for sure.

Maybe tomorrow.

Probably not.

But today Christina could make last forever. The pain would come again and bring with it the nightmares and the nights when sleep wouldn't come, when all she could see were those naked men and women, skeletons who had not yet died, trodding across frozen ground. And the face on every woman was that of her mother.

But not today.

Today she would make John Christy laugh.

After today, there might never be any laughter at all.

Christina had received the phone call shortly after breakfast. On the other end of the line was the unmistakable gravel voice of the American consul.

"Cupid here," he said as he chuckled. "John wants you to know that he and his captain will be arriving in Bydgosczc by train this evening. Can you meet them there?"

For a moment, Christina was speechless.

"Can you hear me?"

"Yes. Yes, I can hear you fine."

"Well, girl, can he expect you to be at the train?"

Christina's heart was pounding wildly, and she was breathless. "Yes, of course. I'll be there."

"And Christina?"

"Yes."

"I still want to know how it turns out."

She hung up the phone and squealed with laughter.

"What's the matter?" Sophie asked when Christina ran into the room, flustered and barely able to breathe.

"It's those crazy Americans."

"What's wrong with them?"

"They're coming here."

"John Christy?"

"He and his captain both."

Sophie looked up from her sewing and raised an eyebrow. "John Christy must really think you're some kind of a Polish firecracker," she teased.

Christina threw her head back and ran her hands through the unruly curls that gathered on her shoulder. "You never know," she replied haughtily. "Maybe I am."

One look in the antique bedroom mirror and her air of self-imposed arrogance quickly faded. The sunlight that filtered through the open window, the leaded glass with its stains and cracks judged her much too harshly. Christina had lost weight, and her clothes merely hung from her fragile shoulders. Her olive skin was almost a milk white, as though the sun had never been allowed to touch it. Her cheeks were sallow, and her eyes were red and sunken, ringed by dark circles and lines she had never noticed before. My God, Christina thought, I look like a corpse.

She sighed and dejectedly ran a comb through the thick curls in her hair.

At the moment, she was convinced that she was staring at a reflection of the ugliest creature she had ever seen. What would John think? What did she expect him to think?

"You're beautiful," he whispered when he at last turned her loose and stepped away, undaunted by the strangers that crowded around them on the railway platform. "I was afraid I couldn't find you again, then I didn't think I would hear from you."

Christina blushed and wondered if she had smudged her makeup. "I'm glad you came, John," she said.

He held her at arm's length and frowned. "I am a little disappointed, though," he told her.

"What's wrong?"

"You're not wearing the American WAC uniform you wrote about from Berlin." He grinned. "I was expecting to see a lady in uniform so I could salute her."

Christina's smile was one of relief.

"But that's all right," John continued. "I love the dress you're wearing. I liked it when you wore it on our last night together in Italy."

He paused and kissed her.

"And I like it even better now," he said.

"You remembered." Christina's eyes brightened, flashing flecks of amber in the late afternoon sunlight.

"There are some things I can't forget." John shrugged.

He felt a not-so-gentle tug on his sleeve. "Well, you sure as hell forgot to introduce me to your lady friend." The drawl was distinct and full of merriment, perhaps slurred somewhat by the liquor that flowed much too freely on the train from Gdansk.

John's shy grin was patronizing. "I'm sorry, Andy," he said, turning to his companion. "Christina, I would like for you to meet my good friend and captain of the *Robert W. Hurt*, William Anderson. We call him Andy to his face and other things behind his back, but he runs a damn good ship."

Andy Anderson clicked his heels together, bowed in an exaggerated fashion, took Christina's hand and kissed it. He probably was no more than two years older than John with blond hair that had obviously been lightened by the sun. He had serious eyes but a happy-go-lucky smile that was both sincere and contagious. Christina doubted that he had ever met a woman he didn't like or one who did not like him immediately.

"Well, John," Andy said, "now I know why you've become something of a hermit. I wouldn't be out hustling other girls either if I had somebody this pretty hidden away in Poland." He winked.

"Thank you." Christina winked back.

John's face reddened. "Andy," he said with indignation, "sometimes I think we ought to keep you locked up when we hit port, or at least make you leave your tongue on the ship when you come ashore."

Andy ignored him, "Christina, for the last four

months, all I've heard John talk about is you. When we get up in the morning. Before we bunk in at night. On watch. On guard. In port. Out at sea. It doesn't matter. I thought the poor boy was lying to me. I guess I owe him an apology."

Christina giggled.

John wore an embarrassed grin.

"Can I have Christina back now?" he asked the captain. "Rank doesn't always have its privileges."

"That's not what the book says."

"I've rewritten the book."

Andy laughed heartily. "Well, I don't blame you," he said. "Any smart man would."

Christina watched the two men carefully as the taxi cab whisked them through downtown Bydgoszcz. Both were wearing their navy blue dress uniforms, freshly pressed, trimmed with gold braid. It made them look older than their years and quite gallant. That was where the similarity ended. Andy was loud and boisterous, John as shy and reserved as he had always been. Andy was looking for action. John had only been looking for her, and she really didn't know why. She was pretty enough, Christina guessed. At any rate, John must have met hundreds of girls throughout the world who were much more beautiful then she. Why had he chosen to come back to her?

He was nice. He was always a gentleman, and she felt comfortable when she was by his side. His was a shoulder she knew she could cry on, and he would never make fun of her, no matter how foolish she might be. He was the strength she needed, especially now. John Christy kept her from being alone, from feeling alone, yet she didn't really understand her feelings for him. They were confused and contradictory.

He was a friend.

That's all.

That's what she told herself.

That's all she would allow herself to believe.

He had come into her life, then he was gone. Perhaps that was what bothered her about John Christy. He was the kind of man she could respect, maybe even love someday. But she would always be telling him goodbye. John Christy would always be leaving, and Christina was merely an overnight stop along the way. He would no doubt forget her in time, and one day she would be too old, too bitter to wait for him anymore.

The taxi pulled up in front of the hotel. Andy had said he wanted the nicest, biggest hotel in town. He got the one that had withstood the bombing and survived the war.

"Does it have rooms?" he asked. "And a bar?"

"Of course."

"Then it'll do just fine."

Christina paced the floor of the lobby while John and Andy checked in and carried their bags up to the room. She was a bundle of nerves, and her stomach was churning with butterflies that wouldn't light anywhere. John was here for the night. But how many nights would there be? What did he expect from her? He had been so quiet on the ride in from the railway station.

She couldn't read his mind.

Maybe she should have let the Gypsy woman read the cards.

When the two men returned, Andy put a strong arm around Christina's shoulder and told her, "My dear, since you're the only native tour guide around here who speaks English, why don't you just take us to the best watering hole you can find in this town."

"I don't understand." Christina looked puzzled.

"A watering hole." Andy laughed. "That's a place where you and John can sip a little wine by candlelight together, and I can get drunk out of my mind." He shrugged. "I may not be having as much fun as you two, but, hell, I won't know it, and come morning I'll be hurting too bad to care."

"You're crazy," Christina said softly.

"The sea'll do that to man," John told her.

"Did it make you crazy?"

"He came halfway around the world by ship and by train on a wild goose chase to Bydgoszcz to look up a little girl who might not even want to see him again." Andy roared with laughter. "What does that tell you."

Christina reached up and kissed John lightly. "Maybe he's a little crazy, too," she agreed.

"Then again," Andy said with a wink, "maybe he's not."

Christina led them around the corner to the Theater Garden, down by the river that wound peacefully through the heart of Bydgoszcz. An outdoor cafe was surrounded by an ice cream parlor and a series of small shops, and they sat beneath a brightly-colored umbrella and watched the sun dip low behind the roses and corn flowers that clustered around a free-flowing fountain.

And grinned, leaned back in his chair, and ordered a beer, dark and bitter. He tilted his cap, breathed deeply and took in the scenery around him with a single glance. "Now this," he said, "is what I call a real watering hole."

It was a gathering place for downtown Bydgoszcz, where white collars and blue collars all drank together from the same cold pitcher. Some were just getting off their jobs. Others had come early for the theater. By six o'clock the working girls had left their shops for the day and were beginning to congregate among the brightly-colored umbrellas, smiling coquettishly at the men who were smiling back at them. They drifted into the cafe in all shapes and sizes and ages, looking for a drink, a dance, some conversation, a good time, a little sympathy, or possibly even new a man to hold tightly while the dance music led them around the floor. It was a place where single women felt sinful, married women felt single, and neither of them ever felt out of place for very long. Behind them a small band was warming up for the long, torrid evening ahead with a Strauss waltz.

Andy leaned forward and asked, "Christina, what's the custom here."

"What do you mean?"

He lowered his voice. "What's the proper procedure for meeting a woman without getting shot?"

"It's not complicated at all, Andy," she whispered. "Just find a pretty girl without a male escort and ask her to dance."

For a moment, he looked flustered. "How?" He shrugged. "I don't speak Polish."

The lilt had returned to Christina's laugh. "You're not going to talk to them," she said gently. "You're going to dance with them. Just hold out your hand. They'll know what you mean."

"I don't know any Polish dances."

"Don't worry." She giggled. "Neither do they."

Andy stood, started toward the dance floor, then stopped and leaned down beside Christina again.

"What'll I do if one of them says something to me?"

"Just say yes," Christina whispered, "and take your chances."

Andy winked again and was gone.

"He's a nice man," Christina said to John.

"He's a good man."

"I'm glad that he was thoughtful enough to leave us alone for awhile." The evening shadows had begun to stretch across the garden, and the roses beside the fountain were a deeper red than Christina had ever noticed before.

John reached out and caressed the softness of her neck with his fingertips. He grinned. "At least I'll have you to myself until Andy gets back."

Christina glanced toward the dance floor and saw the

captain dancing snugly against a long-legged brunette whose skirt should have been longer and whose eyelashes should have been shorter and not nearly so black. Andy Anderson didn't have to speak Polish. When his lady friend danced, she was telling him everything she knew. "I don't think Andy's coming back," Christina said.

"Then it's just you and me," John said softly, raising his glass of Chablis to toast her.

"For how long?"

John was taken aback. Christina's sudden bluntness had startled him.

She lowered her eyes, and her words were barely audible. "I mean, how much time do we have together before you have to go back to your ship."

Christina was afraid to breathe.

"Four days."

Her face lit up with surprise, radiant in the golden afterglow of sundown.

"We don't sail until the afternoon of the eleventh," John said.

Christina's eyes moistened.

Four days, she thought.

Four glorious days.

She couldn't believe it. It was so much more than she had dared hope for, and Christina could feel the laughter swelling up within her, ready to burst out at any moment. Maybe there was a God in heaven after all. Maybe, just maybe, He really was looking out for her.

She had doubted.

But not anymore.

John was there, and he was with her, and he would be with her for four days.

Four glorious days.

For Christina, it could be a lifetime.

"Do you want to dance?" he asked her.

"No. I just want to sit here and look at you. It's been a

long time, John. A lot can happen in four months."

"I haven't changed any."

His smile embarrassed Christina, then saddened her. "I'm afraid I have," she said softly.

John refilled their glasses with Chablis and nodded to a waiter to bring them another bottle, chilled this time, on ice if possible.

His eyes grew solemn, his voice grave. "What's wrong, Christina?" he asked, taking her hand in his, surprised at how cold and lifeless it felt.

"What do you mean?"

"You're trembling."

"It must be the wine." Christina looked away.

"No. It's not the wine." John's brow was furrowed with worry and concern. "It's something else, something you're hiding from me. You're not the same vibrant, carefree little girl I met and left behind in Italy. You were like a butterfly then, beautiful and elusive, unpredictable and impossible to catch or even hold for very long." He drew her closer to him and looked into the sorrow that lingered deep in her eyes. "The beauty is still there," he continued. "But the happiness is gone." He shook his head sadly. "The butterfly has flown and I don't know where to find it."

Christina leaned her head on his shoulder. "I'm sorry I've disappointed you," she said, her voice breaking.

John put an arm around her. "I'm not disappointed. I could never be disappointed with you, Christina." He kissed her and tasted the salt from the tears that stained her face. And again he asked, "What's wrong, Christina?"

For a long time she didn't answer. She just sat there in the warmth, the comfort of his arms. Christina silently scolded herself. This should be the happiest moment she had had since John Christy first kissed her without any warning on a chilly night in Trieste. Now she had ruined it. For him. For her. Forever. She couldn't stop crying now, no matter how hard she tried, and that angered her. Christina pulled away from him.

"I want to dance now," was all she said.

John followed her out onto the crowded dance floor while the band played a love song he had never heard before. Christina found refuge in the darkness. John might sense her distress, but he couldn't see her face, and she knew it must be a mess. She didn't want to talk anymore. Not now. Christina watched a new moon hang crookedly in the night sky.

"I want to meet your family while I'm here," John said when the music had stopped.

"My Aunt Sophie and Uncle Kostek are planning dinner for us tomorrow night." Christina replied. "Eight o'clock. I hope that's all right."

"That sounds great." He tilted Christina's face toward him. "But I also want to meet your parents."

"You can't," she snapped.

"But it's important that I do."

"It's quite impossible, and I don't want to talk about it." Christina whirled around and fled the dance floor, pushing her way roughly through startled couples who crowded around the band, staring awkwardly at the impertinent girl whose face was a mess and who had broken the romantic moods of Johann Strauss. John caught her as she ran among the roses and cornflowers that clustered together along the outer garden wall.

He stared at her, his eyes full of unanswered questions.

She met his gaze and never wavered.

"It was a mistake for you to come here," Christina said tersely, her fists clenched tightly at her side.

"But I missed you."

"It was a mistake for me to come back, too."

"But this is your home."

"I have no home."

"But your parents are here," John argued.

"I have no parents."

John's shoulders sagged as he began to understand the reason for her discontent, the depth of her sadness.

"They're dead," she said. "My mother . . . my father . . . my grandmother . . . my Aunt Jadwega. The SS killed them all. In the Katowice forest, in Auschwitz. It doesn't matter. They weren't people. They were just a number that had to be erased, and the SS erased them."

"What happened to them?" John was visibly shaken.

Christina looked again at the new moon, and a curious smile crossed her face. "They just walked away one day," she said, "and they never came back." Her voice trailed off.

John held her close, and felt her body stiffen at his touch. "How can I help?" he asked.

"You can't."

"But I can try."

"Can you?"

Christina stepped back and stared at him, her face pinched and twisted with bitterness. The warmth had vanished from her eyes, and she looked as though John were a stranger, an intruder she no longer wanted in her life.

"You have everything, John," she said, her voice brittle with envy. "Your family . . . your ship . . . your career. And now you want me. But for how long, John? Tonight? Tomorrow? For four days? Then I'll wake up and you'll be gone, and what will I have left, John? A promise that you'll come back some day?"

John never flinched, even though her stinging words cut him deeply. He stood as if at attention, his shoulders square and his chin firm and strong.

Christina's black eyes flashed with anger.

"You'll have everything, John," she said accusingly. "And I'll wake up with nothing."

His expression masked the feelings boiling inside him.

"Nothing!" Christina spit the word out and it left a bad taste in her mouth.

She stood, her legs spread apart, her hands on her hips, a look of stubborn defiance on her face. Christina had held her grief inside for as long as she could stand it. It had eaten away at her like a malignancy she could not cure, and now it had exploded all over John Christy.

Right now, she thought, he probably hated her.

She didn't blame him.

She didn't care.

She was just tired of being kicked around and dragged through a world that had gone sour. She just didn't want to be hurt anymore.

Then she saw the hurt embedded in his eyes.

"I love you, Christina," John said, his throat dry, his voice sanded to a whisper.

His words jarred her.

She stepped back, afraid to believe what she had heard, and watched the dim moonlight frame his face. John had, she told herself, the most beautiful smile she had ever seen. That's what she had liked best about him. That's what she had remembered most during the sleepless nights that haunted her return to Poland.

John waited for her to answer.

Christina had grown silent, watchful. He saw the tension melt away from her face. Her anger, her unexpected outburst had drained her emotionally, and, for a moment, John thought she was going to faint.

He put an arm around Christina's waist to steady her, and she fell heavily against him, the strength sapped from her body. John buried his face in the tangled mass of her curls and whispered softly, "I think I fell in love with you after our first date in Trieste. Now I know that I did. I'm more convinced than ever that I love you and always will."

"You don't even know me."

He laughed gently. "I don't think anybody does."

"Doesn't that bother you?"

"It only bothers me to think about losing you."

"But you will."

"I'm not planning on it."

Christina sighed and turned away from him. "Four days," she said, and her words hung stoically in the wind.

"I don't understand."

"Four days," Christina said sharply. "That's all we have together. That's all we may ever have."

"I'll be back."

Christina smiled sadly. "You may think you will." She shrugged. "The sea may have other ideas."

"I won't be coming back just to see you."

John reached into his pocket and pulled out a small red velvet box and placed it gingerly in her hand. She opened it and saw two plain, simple, golden wedding bands glittering in the pale light of the moon.

"I'll be coming back to get you," he said.

Christina looked up at him with disbelief.

"I want to marry you as soon as possible. That's why I'm here," John continued, and he saw the faint spark that had been missing from Christina's eyes. "That's the reason I asked to see your parents. I wanted your permission and their blessing."

For the first time, Christina smiled, ever so coyly. "Papa would have probably said no," she said. "But he would have liked you very, very much."

"Then I'm asking you," John said. He shifted his weight nervously and didn't like the way he felt. "I want to marry you before I have to leave, then take you with me to America as soon as you can get your papers in order."

"That may take time," Christina heard herself say.

"I've waited this long."

Christina sat down beside the fountain and lay back

among the flowers. She touched the rings and a chill she had never experienced before shot like a lightning bolt through her body. They were so beautiful, just like John's smile. She looked at him as he knelt beside her.

He said he loved her.

No man had ever told her that before. The thought both excited her and confused her.

But how did she feel about John? Christina didn't really know. He wanted to carry her home with him. He had promised that much. And John would take care of her—she had no doubts about that at all.

But she didn't love him. Not yet anyway.

Maybe she never would. Then again, maybe she would be in love by morning.

Christina pulled John's face close to hers and kissed him youthfully and shamelessly as the shadow from a passing cloud held them tightly together amidst the roses and the thorns.

Chapter 14

FATHER JOSEPH MATUSZAK never took his eyes off Christina as they sat together in a small courtyard behind St. Elizabeth Church. She had virtually dragged him out of his study early that morning, her face aglow and chattering incessantly about marrying some American naval officer she had only seen five times in her whole life. The parish priest shook his head in dismay, totally bewildered at the thought of anyone so young doing anything so foolish at such an uncertain time in her life.

He had met with Christina often during the past few weeks, listening as she expunged the grief and anger, the hate and frustration from her soul. Father Matuszak had worried about her then. He worried about her still. As far as he was concerned, she just simply wasn't old enough nor wise enough to make such decisions that would last her a lifetime. That's what he had told her, but as usual, Christina wouldn't listen to him. He grinned laconically, sometimes quite convinced that he was only wasting his time as the shepherd of a flock who might not even need him. The priest in all of his forty-seven years had never been able to understand why parishioners came to him for advice, then chose to ignore it as soon as they left the shadow of the church.

He was beginning to grow uncomfortable now that the sun had risen high enough to chase away the morning chill, and he didn't know whether it was the heat or Christina's plight that was bothering him so. Even the birds had stopped their singing, and the humidity hung wet and heavy on his shoulders.

Father Matuszak knew Christina about as well as anyone. He had held her as a baby, heard her first prayers, had even given Christina her first communion, back when days were calm and no one wore the unhealed scars of war.

Now Christina wanted him to stand before God and say the words that would join her and a stranger in holy wedlock.

Father Joseph Matuszak was a troubled man.

He had watched the anguish twist Christina's face, seen the tears flow down her cheeks, knew how far and how deep she had fallen into the depths of her own personal hell. He had sometimes wondered late at night, when he knelt alone to pray for her, if he would ever see Christina smile again.

Now there was a light in her eyes that hadn't been there before, and the pain had loosened its angry grip on her face. Christina obviously knew what she wanted. But did she know what was best for her? Did anyone?

Father Matuszak stood and walked across the courtyard, beads of sweat gathering on his deeply-furrowed forehead. He looked down at Christina, his hands folded reverently beneath his chin, and asked the question he dreaded most.

"Is John a Catholic?"

"No."

The priest waited for her to continue.

Christina glanced nervously away. "He's a Lutheran," she said.

Father Matuszak frowned. Christina certainly wasn't making his decision any easier for him. "I can't encourage you to marry anyone outside your faith," he told her.

"I know," she whispered.

The priest sat down beside Christina and, with his fingertips, turned her face toward him.

"Do you love John?" he asked.

"He loves me."

"How do you know?"

Christina sighed wistfully, and an innocent smile crossed her face. "John didn't forget me," she said. "He could have, but he didn't. Before he left me on our last night together in Trieste, John promised that he would look for me and find me no matter where I went."

"Did you believe him?"

"No." Christina laughed aloud. "I thought he was just a crazy American who didn't know how to say goodbye. I never expected to se him again."

"So you forgot John."

"I tried. It was foolish to keep thinking about him. He was on one side of the world, and I was on the other. John kept writing me letters, but I just thought he was probably bored and had too much time on his hands at sea." Christina shrugged with embarrassment. "I wrote him back a few times, feeling that he would only throw my letters away."

"Did he?"

Christina shook her head. "He kept them. John told me he knew that he would find me somehow, some way, if he had to search from one end of Europe to the other." Her words began trail off. "He almost did."

Father Matuszak grinned. "Well, he's a persistent young man. I'll give him credit for that."

"While John was in America," Christina continued, "he went to a jewelry store and bought wedding rings. He wanted to marry me then. He still does." Christina abruptly turned to the priest, an urgent pleading in her voice. "I know he loves me, Father. No man would have done what John did unless he loved me."

For a moment, an uneasy silence separated the priest and the girl who was begging him to turn his back on his beliefs, on the rules of his church, on his personal conviction. It would be a mistake to marry Christina and John. In his heart, he was sure of it. Yet, it might be a greater mistake if he did not. Father Joseph Matuszak rose from the aging, weathered bench and walked slowly back toward the church, wrestling with his own conscience. He didn't want Christina hurt. God knows, she had already been hurt enough. As much as anyone, she deserved her chance to find a measure of love and happiness in a world that sometimes seemed devoid of love and happiness. Yet there was a serious doubt nagging at the back of the priest's mind. He had asked Christina the most important question of all, the one most women could answer without even thinking about it. And she had quietly evaded the question. Maybe, she was afraid of the answer. Maybe she was afraid of the truth.

Father Matuszak, his face grim and thoughtful, asked again, "Christina, do you love John?"

She stared at him with disturbed eyes.

"I don't know," she said.

He barely heard her, and the pain again tightened its grip on Christina's face.

Father Matuszak stood beside Christina and placed a firm, but gentle, hand on her shoulder.

"Are you frightened, child?" he asked.

She nodded.

"You can never run away," the priest told her. "You can try, but it won't do you any good. No matter how far you go, the past will always be right behind you, lingering like a shadow, there when you go to sleep at night, still there when you awaken the next morning. You can't run away from reality, Christina. you have to face it."

"I am facing it," she snapped testily.

"You're afraid of it." Father Matuszak raised his voice, throwing up his arms in frustration.

"Let me tell you what reality is." Christina stood face to face with the priest, her eyes flashing. "The reality is my mother is gone, my father is gone, my home is gone, and I'm living with my aunt like an orphan, and I'm much too old for that. The reality is I have nothing left in Bydgoszcz; I have nothing left in Poland. The reality is I'm nineteen years old and have to face the rest of my life, and I don't want to face it alone. The reality is John says he loves me and will take care of me, and that's something very important to me, Father. That's a lot more than I have here. That's a lot more than I may ever have here."

"You're a dreamer."

"Maybe."

"A hopeless romantic."

"Probably."

"What happens if John suddenly decides one day that he doesn't want you anymore."

"I only care that he wants me now."

"Does John even know what love is?"

"He knows how he feels."

"Love doesn't always last forever, and sometimes it doesn't exist at all." Father Matuszak's voice hardened. "You're a foreign girl in a foreign land," the priest said harshly. "John is intrigued with you. For him, you are forbidden fruit, and that makes you even more desirable. He says he wants you now, Christina, but is it love, or is it merely lust? Will he still want you when he goes back home? Or more importantly, Christina, will you want him?"

Christina gazed out across the roses and cornflowers

that brought a rich splash of color to the church garden. They had wilted beneath a summer sun that was beating down without mercy from a parched sky, and the color was fading before her eyes. She knew that Father Matuszak had always had her best interest at heart, even now. He sometimes angered her. He sometimes frustrated her. He was like a strict parent who usually said things his children didn't like to hear, didn't want to hear, regardless of how right or how wrong they might be. He was simply concerned about her now and about her future.

Until John walked back into her life. Christina hadn't thought much about her future at all. She wasn't even sure if she had one. Now John had taken her into his arms and brought hope and promise back into her life. Was that reason enough to marry a man she didn't really know? Doubt and indecision began to slowly strangle the exuberance that Christina had felt when she awoke that morning.

Maybe Father Matuszak was right, she told herself. Maybe John was simply an escape, a way out of the agony, the misery that haunted her dreams even when she had trouble sleeping at night. John was so kind and gentle in a world that had gone mad and crumbled around her shoulders.

He offered her everything. He offered her love.

Did she have any love to offer him in return?

The ache cut deep into Christina's soul, and the hope that had been so strong that morning began to wilt and fade like the flowers at her feet.

She looked at Father Matuszak and tried to smother the alarm she felt rising up within her.

"I'll be a good wife," Christina said solemnly.

It was a simple, yet powerful, vow made to him, before God, that the priest would never quite forget.

He sighed. His meeting with Christina had come to an end. He couldn't argue with her. Perhaps it had been a sin to even try. Christina was spoiled. He knew that.

And, she was obstinate. He knew that he could refuse to perform the marriage ceremony, and the church would stand behind him. But he was no longer convinced that that would be the right thing to do. He was no longer living in a world that always knew the difference between right or wrong. Christina had sworn to him that she would be a good wife, and he had no reason to doubt her.

Father Matuszak hugged her reassuringly. "I'll talk to John," he said, and a strange calm that he could not explain fell over him as he walked away from the courtyard and entered again into the candle-lit sanctity of the church.

The priest knelt before the hand-carved, wooden crucifix that hung above the altar and clasped his hands together in prayer. What he was contemplating, he knew, was strongly opposed by all orders of the church. If he decided to marry Christina and John, he would have to bend the rules of the Catholic faith, if not break them outright.

Father Matuszak sighed. It wouldn't be the first time he had defied the teachings, the edicts of Rome. When war had broken out on Polish soil, he had received word to remain in the church and out of the conflict. A priest, he was told, had no business becoming involved with the issues, regardless of his own personal ideas or beliefs. He must remain neutral. He must remain quiet. Father Matuszak had looked around and watched the horror of the holocaust as it began to unfold in the crematoriums of Auschwitz. The silent screams kept him awake at night. The dying seared his tortured conscience. The church turned its head and looked the other way. Father Joseph Matuszak could not. He quietly arranged for the escape of thirteen Jewish families to England, virtually smuggling them out from beneath the acrid smoke of Hitler's guns.

The church condemned him.

The Germans jailed him.

Two weeks later, he was released. No one in the parish ever knew what had happened. Father Matuszak would not talk about it. The arrest was the sin, the secret, the disgrace, the triumph he would carry with him alone to his grave.

As he knelt in the dim light of the chapel, he realized that the church would again have a hard time forgiving him. Its wrath was probably justified. Father Matuszak had already been branded a maverick priest, and it was a charge that he no longer defended. He merely did what he thought should be done and accepted the consequences.

The priest smiled a tired smile and closed his eyes. Maybe God would understand, he hoped. Nobody else ever did. He crossed himself and bowed his head, his black robe masked by the darkness of the sanctuary. "Father," he said, "forgive me for what I am about to do."

John Christy came to him in the shank of the afternoon, a Protestant in an enemy camp.

Father Matuszak wasted no time in coming to the point. In broken English, he told John, "Christina has been raised in the Catholic Church all of her life and will never leave it. It's important to her. It's part of her heritage."

John nodded.

"If you have children," the priest asked bluntly, "in what faith will they be raised?"

John didn't hesitate. "In whatever faith their mother wants them raised," he said.

"You won't stand in their way of becoming Catholic?"

"No."

Father Matuszak paused, and his eyes cut sharply toward the officer, standing at attention in the twilight of the day, dressed in his blue uniform with gold braid.

John Christy met his gaze and never wavered.

The priest stepped forward and spoke slowly, making

sure that John could understand every word he said. He might be a maverick. He might bend some rules and break others. But there was one thing he would not tolerate.

"In Poland," he snapped curtly, "divorce is unheard of."

"Divorce scarred my life." John replied, his voice firm and steady. "I would never let it scar anyone else's."

"Do you love Christina?"

"As much as life itself."

"Can you make her happy?"

"I can do my dead level best."

Father Matuszak had always prided himself in being able to discern a man's character by reading his eyes. In John, he saw strength and compassion and loyalty. He was a good man, young but mature far beyond his age. He was so much like the Polish boys who had stood together on the banks of the Vistula in Warsaw, a fragile chain of resistence rising up in the face of the German juggernaut that rolled over them with the frenzy of a maddened beast. They were doomed from the first shot, and they knew it. But none would run. They were too proud. They were too stubborn. They fought boldly and bravely with hand-me-down rifles and homemade bombs until there was no one left to die. Their blood stained Polish soil, but never their shame. Father Matuszak had prayed with them, had blessed them, had buried them. He believed in them. He knew he could believe in John Christy just as easily.

"It is customary in our country to wait three months before the wedding ceremony is performed." the priest said.

"I don't have that much time," John replied.

"How much time do you have."

"I must leave here day after tomorrow. My ship sails early the next morning."

Father Matuszak frowned and leaned back in the

plain, oaken chair behind his desk. "That does present something of a problem then doesn't it?" It was a statement, not a question. The priest rubbed his chin and glanced toward the ceiling, lost for a moment in his own agonizing thoughts.

"Of course," he said mostly to himself, "you must get permission from the Polish government in order to marry a Polish girl."

Now it was John's turn to frown.

"And," Father Matuszak added, "you must get permission from the Russian government as well."

"What procedures do I follow to get that done?" John asked him.

"Oh, that would be a useless venture and a waste of your time," Father Matuszak answered matter-of-factly. "I'm afraid that neither the Poles nor the Russians will give you permission to marry."

"Why not?"

"Simple." The priest grinned sympathetically. "You're an American. And, you see, they aren't interested in losing anything to an American these days, especially one of their women."

John was stunned.

"Then what'll I do?"

"The Lord will provide."

John laughed caustically. "It's a little late to pray isn't it?"

The priest's smile faded. "It's never too late," he admonished. Father Matuszak stood and walked around his small reading desk, his hands clasped at his waist. The sun had dropped down behind the churchyard wall, and the dim light of early evening had left the room dark and full of shadows. "Don't worry, John," the priest continued. "I'll have a legal marriage certificate ready for you day after tomorrow."

John was skeptical. "How are you going to accomplish that?" he asked.

Father Matuszak arched an eyebrow, and an enigmatic smile moved across his face. "God moves in mysterious ways," he said quietly, "and sometimes, so do his servants."

He picked up his *Bible*, turned his back on John Christy, and began to read silently to himself. As far as he was concerned, the matter was closed. All he had left to worry about now were the necessary details that needed to be worked out. Father Matuszak knew he didn't have much time, but he had enough. It was, he told himself, a good thing that he still believed in miracles. God didn't perform many anymore—at least not in his presence. But Father Matuszak had been known to weave a miracle or two when the need arose, and, whether he liked it or not, the need had arisen again.

John awoke early on the morning of July 10. He hadn't been able to sleep at all during the night, and his back ached from lying on a hotel mattress that had been broken in, worn down, and worn out years ago. The lumps had lumps, and he hoped his wedding night wouldn't be spent in the same kind of bed, then decided it didn't really matter. He yawned, smiled inwardly, and got dressed, watching the sunrise pierce the sky from his hotel window. The gathering clouds in the east were streaked with several shades of gold, and the day was already promising to be as hot and as relentless as the one before. John wondered if Christina were awake yet and doubted seriously if she had slept any better than he had.

He had held her close to him until long after midnight, walking down empty streets that kept leading them through the faint, sometimes bitter memories of her childhood. John knew so little about Christina, yet he was convinced that she, and she alone, was the one vital spark that had been missing from his life. Christina was laughter in a world that had forgotten how to laugh. She was love in a land where, for most, love had become a commodity with silk stockings and a price tag. She was independent. She had spirit. She was genuine. In Italy, John has been fascinated by Christina. While at sea, he was infatuated with her. Now he was convinced that he could not live without her. At least he didn't want to try.

The taxicab slowly threaded its way through a city determined to rebuild itself from the rubble, the ashes of its own ruins. Workmen were sweating in the streets early, and armed Russian soldiers patrolled the crowded thoroughfares, warily watching each vehicle that passed their way. John Christy ignored them. He had more important matters on his mind.

He was sure that Christina had broken the news to her aunt by now, and he wondered what she and Uncle Kostek had thought about the sudden, unexpected wedding of their only niece. They had eyed John coolly the first night he visited in their home, not quite sure who he was and why he had come so far just to see Christina. Now they knew. John, more or less, had received Father Matuszak's blessing, but he wanted their blessing as well. By tomorrow night, he would be part of Christina's family, and he did not want Sophie or Kostek to hold any kind of grudge against him. She needed them. She needed them to accept her decision to marry John Christy.

"Aunt Sophie likes you," Christina had whispered to him as they walked along the Utza Dolina the night before. "She thinks you're handsome."

John had an embarrassed grin.

"Well, she didn't exactly call you handsome," Christina giggled. "But she did say that you were no ugly duckling."

John blushed and was glad that the darkness hid his red face. "How about your Uncle Kostek?" he asked. "What does he think about me?"

Christina shrugged. "He's suspicious of you."

"Because I'm an American?"

"Because you're a man."

"Why?"

"Because he's a man, and he knows how you men think." Christina laughed.

John chuckled. "I think he's misjudged me."

"No." Christina's eyes twinkled. "He's judged you correctly. He knows you want to take me to bed with you. He just doesn't know that you want me to go to bed as your wife."

"He's got a lot to learn."

Christina glanced away. "So have I," she said shyly.

They had stood beneath the harsh glow of a street corner gaslight, trapped together by time and circumstance and hope, and John hugged her tightly as the night winds gently rustled through the trees that encircled them. He felt the softness of her body press eagerly against him, and she quivered ever so slightly when he kissed her. Christina was so beautiful. She was so tempting. She was so unlike any woman that he had ever met before. He kept forgetting that she was so young. John didn't take her home until she had fallen asleep in his arms. He had been whistling then.

He was whistling still as he paid his taxi fare and bounded up the steps to the front door of the Colonialka.

Aunt Sophie had liked him last night.

He wondered what her thoughts were now.

"You've lost your mind," Sophie screamed at Christina as John walked into the store.

She was standing there in the middle of the room, hands on her hips, eyes ablaze with disappointment and rage. Kostek had merely turned and walked away, slowly shaking his head, retreating as far away as possible from the fight. A *smart* man, he had always said, knew when to keep his mouth shut. A *wise* man knew when to get the hell out of his wife's way.

"But John loves me," Christina screamed back, ignoring all of Sophie's attempts to reason with her.

"It doesn't make any difference. You still can't marry him tomorrow."

"I'm old enough to know what's best for me."

"You're crazy." Sophie waved her arms in total and complete frustration.

"Why do you hate John?"

"I don't hate John." Sophie turned and pointed toward him. "He's a good man. He's straightforward. He's educated. He has good manners. Your parents would have liked him a lot. I like him a lot. Even Kostek likes him."

Sophie snapped her head back toward Christina, removed her apron and threw it angrily into the corner. "But what you are too stubborn to realize, Christina, is that you have not given me enough time to plan for or prepare a proper wedding breakfast. There is no way I can put one together on such a short notice that either one of us would be proud of."

Christina broke out in laughter.

"I don't want breakfast," she said. "I want a husband."

"It's tradition," Sophie replied curtly, her chin thrust forward in defiance. "In this family, in this household, no one gets married without an official wedding breakfast. No one ever has. As long as I'm alive, no one ever will."

John cleared his throat and stepped between the two women. Both looked on him as an intruder.

"Pardon me, Sophie," he said politely. "I appreciate what you want to do for Christina. I know she does, too. And I'm well aware that we haven't been able to give you the time you need to prepare for a breakfast. But I'm afraid my ship sails day after tomorrow, and I have to be on it, and I don't want to leave Christina unless I leave her as my wife. I hope you understand."

He paused.

Christina's smile was one of pride and gratitude.

Sophie glared at him, her eyes as black as coals and almost as searing.

"Thank you for your offer, Sophie," John continued. "But I certainly don't want to cause you an inconvenience. With your approval, I would like to personally host the breakfast at my hotel and at my expense."

Sophie's mouth gaped open. Her face reddened.

For a moment, Christina thought her aunt's temper would explode all over John.

Sophie shoved a crooked finger in his chest, and asked in a shrill voice, "Are you trying to deny me the privilege of having a wedding reception for the only niece I have or will ever have?"

"No, ma'am."

"Then be off with you," she shouted. "I have work to do, and I certainly don't have time for you to stand here in the middle of my own house arguing with me."

John backed toward the front door. He didn't quite know whether to walk or run. He ventured a glance at Christina and couldn't remember when she had looked so radiant, although he wasn't sure whether she was flushed with happiness or from the confrontation with her aunt. He winked.

He should have known Christina would get her way. She always did. Probably, he decided, she always would.

Christina tilted her head and brushed aside the curls that framed her face. There was a haughty glint in her eyes that made her look much older than she had the night before. She winked back.

John Christy strolled back out into the morning sunshine. His first thought was to find the hotel, awaken Andy Anderson, pour hot coffee down him, to sober him up, then do his damndest to get them both drunk before night fell. He laughed. He might as well. This would be the last day of his life that he would ever be single.

The morning of July 11, dawned bright and sunny, the

way John Christy had expected it to. He stood in the candlelight of St. Elizabeth Church, watching gray shadows as they flickered across the painted faces of archangels on the ceiling, then danced lightly down the stone wall, caught in a rainbow of color that had been left by the sudden bursts of sunshine through stained glass.

Father Matuszak had told him earlier, "I will marry you and Christina. But because you are not Catholic, John, I cannot perform the ceremony in front of the altar."

"As long as it's in the eyes of God."

The priest had grinned. "I don't make many promises," he said, "but that's one I will guarantee you."

So John stood with Father Matuszak behind the altar and waited for Christina to appear. Beside him, his best man, Andy Anderson, was at attention, formal, dignified, and erect, which, John realized, was quite an accomplishment considering the amount of Polish beer he had consumed the night before.

The summer heat was sweltering inside the chapel, even though the hour was early. Most weddings took place at two o'clock in the afternoon. But on this particular morning, Father Matuszak, at the last minute, had changed the time to 10:00 A.M. He had his reasons, he said. Neither the Polish nor the Russian authorities had been notified of the wedding ceremony, and he did not want to arouse their suspicion or their curiosity. What God had joined together would be no problem at all for the Russians to unravel by nightfall, and Father Matuszak had no desire at all to see anyone begin the first hours of their married life separated and alone in a jail cell somewhere on the forgotten side of Bgydoszcz. His idea was to simply join Christina Skiba and John Christy in holy wedlock, wish them Godspeed, and then send them on their way out of town as quickly as possible. Maybe no one would ever know. Secrets were hard to keep in an occupied city, but the priest had kept them before.

Andy began to sway back and forth, and sweat stained the collar of his blue uniform. John smiled inwardly. He knew full well that his captain would be much more comfortable on the bow of his ship with a strong north wind blowing in his face. He followed Father Matuszak's stern but compassionate gaze to the narrow, hand-carved doorway that entered into the sanctuary from an arched corridor connecting the sacristy to the courtyard. For John, it was an expectant moment.

He drew a deep breath. Christina, her oval face brushed gently by candlelight, stepped into the chapel. It was the first time he had seen her since the chimes of the church bell began striking twelve the night before.

Christina, without warning, had suddenly kissed him and run into her aunt's store, slamming the door behind her, leaving him standing alone and perplexed on the front porch.

John had banged on the door. "What's wrong?" he shouted.

"It's midnight."

"We're always out past midnight."

"Not tonight."

"Why?"

"I'm superstitious." There was a hint of amusement in her voice on the far side of the door, and John could imagine her laughing at him.

"About what?"

"I'm getting married tomorrow."

"So am I. But I didn't run off and leave you."

"It's unlucky for the groom to see his bride on the day their wedding until she walks into the chapel."

Now she was walking toward him, and the vibrant smile in her eyes matched the one on her face. John had never seen her more beautiful, more assure of herself.

She was no longer just a mere nineteen/year-old girl on the threshold of life. She had the glow of womanhood radiating around her face.

John glanced at the engagement ring she was wearing proudly on the third finger of her left hand, and he almost chuckled aloud. It had been a last- minute, absurd, and probably unnecessary thought that sent him and Christina hurrying madly like children through the downtown streets of Bgydoszcz, frantically searching for a reputable jeweler before the stores had all closed for the night.

He had bought the matching wedding bands months ago, carrying them everywhere he went, hoping to find Christina, waiting for the day she would be in his arms again. But for some reason—he himself didn't even understand why—John had neglected to buy an engagement ring.

"I don't really need one," Christina had told him.

"Of course you do," John insisted. "That's the way we do things in America. First you wear the engagement ring, then the wedding ring."

Christina kissed him. "You're just a romantic," she teased.

"Only when I'm in love."

And he was in love—hopelessly so. There was nothing John could do about it except make sure that Christina had every thing she deserved on the most important day of their lives together. He had grabbed her hand, yelled for a taxi, and sent the driver toward the heart of town as the long shadows of late afternoon inched their way across the gabled rooftops of Bgydoszcz.

The aging jeweler they found watched them with bored indifference. It was late. He was obviously tired and ready to go home for the day, jaded somewhat and no longer affected by young couples in love who came to look at his diamonds.

Christina picked up a ring and watched it sparkle in

the dying rays of a setting sun.

"It's lovely," she said softly.

He slipped it on her finger.

"It fits perfectly." Christina lay her head against John's shoulder.

"Then that's the one you should have," he replied.

Her smile faded slightly. "But it must be so expensive," she said.

John turned to the jeweler. "How much for the ring?" he asked.

The jeweler frowned and rubbed a gnarled hand across his balding head. He stared at John a moment as a wary smile touched his lips, then he inquired, "Are you American?"

John nodded in reply.

"Do you have American cigarettes with you?"

"I can get them."

The jeweler lifted Christina's hand close to his face and intensely studied the gold ring's three-diamond setting. Finally he looked at John and said flatly, "It will cost you four cartons of American cigarettes."

John shook his head in disbelief. "Is that all?" he asked cautiously.

"For you, it may not be so much," the jeweler answered. "But that is because you have American cigarettes. I don't. Money, I can get. But American cigarettes are as precious to me as diamonds are to you."

"I have them at my hotel."

The jeweler grinned broadly, and his teeth were stained the yellow of his gold. "I'll wait," he said. Suddenly it wasn't so late, and he wasn't so tired, and he could go home anytime. He reached under the counter, pulled out two crystal champagne glasses, and handed them to Christina. "For you," he told her. "I hope you are as happy a year from now as you are today." He clasped her hands together and patted them in a fatherly fashion.

She smiled her gratitude.

She was still smiling, her cheeks flushed, her eyes as bright as the diamonds on her left hand.

Only one thing was wrong. Since childhood, Christina had dreamed of wearing a long, flowing bridal gown, white and trimmed with chantilly lace. Her wedding would be one of great magnitude in a church crowded with people, and she would be supported by a dozen attendants, all dressed alike, all dressed in pink with matching lace to form their veils. That's the way it would be. Christina had always been so sure of it.

Now the church was virtually empty. Aunt Sophie and Uncle Kostek, along with a few neighbors who had not been afraid to defy Russian authorities, were gathered together on the first row of wooden pews. There had been no time for any one to make a long, flowing bridal gown. That was out of the question, and there were none in town to be bought for any price. So Christina had chosen to wear a cream silk blouse under a light beige suit, and she had a garland of blue cornflowers in her hair. There was no veil. There was no lace. There was no long line of beautiful attendants stretched out behind her, only a plain-looking second cousin who she had not seen in ten years to stand nervously with her as maid of honor.

One dream had been shattered.

But John had brought to her another.

She said her vows, and her frail, trembling voice echoed among the gray stone walls of St. Elizabeth Church. She heard her aunt quietly crying, and she tightened her grip on John's hand. Maybe, in a way, Father Matuszak had been right, she thought. John was her escape. He was her chance to begin again and begin anew.

Soon the anguish of Poland would be behind her.

Soon she would be stepping ashore in a new world, America: the home of the brave and the land of the free. It sounded so wonderful to her, full of hope and opportunity, a country unscarred by war or chaos in the aftermath of war, a place far away where she and John could find their peace on earth. There had been times when Christina doubted that such a place existed at all. The dull ache in her heart was for her mother, her father, her homeland. All were just a fading memory, even now, and she wasn't even gone.

In the silence of a Polish morning, with the archangels looking down upon her and Russian soldiers marching outside past the stained glass window, Christina Skiba, for now and forever, became Mrs. John Christy.

The wedding breakfast back at Sophie's home was a maze of faces, old and new, familiar and strange, of laughter and tears and goodbyes. Her aunt's neighbors had spent all night in the kitchen, juggling pots and pans of all sizes between their houses, cooking and baking and spreading a feast that Christina would never forget. She wasn't supposed to forget. Aunt Sophie made sure of it. On one table lay the wedding presents, mostly heirlooms of linens, china, and crystal. Christina looked at them through blurred eyes. She would be leaving someday soon, but she would be taking part of her Polish heritage with her.

She looked nervously at John.

He glanced at the clock.

"It's time to go," he whispered.

They were on the train, speeding toward the coastal town of Sopot, before most of Aunt Sophie's guests even knew they were gone. She and Kostek stood at the window and stared after them, then turned back to the celebration that would continue on until long after the liquor was consumed and the men, with crooked grins on their well-soaked faces, had dropped in their tracks. Sophie sighed and pushed the hair from her eyes. She hoped that Elizabeth would have approved of the wedding. She knew she could never hope to take the place of

Christina's mother, but she had done her best, and that's all she could do.

Inside her room at the Hotel Internationale in Sopot, Christina sat in the darkness and waited for her head to clear itself of the cobwebs that too much champagne had spun there. She could hear John's steady breathing, feel his arm around her waist, and she quivered with anticipation at his touch. For awhile, he simply lay there in the quiet of the evening, and neither of them spoke.

Tonight they would be as one.

Tomorrow, John would be at sea and she would be alone again. But that was tomorrow. And tomorrow was a sunrise away.

Christina smiled to herself and lay back in the arms of a stranger who was her husband.

Chapter 15

CHRISTINA HAD TAKEN THE NIGHT TRAIN to Warsaw, and was standing beside the door to the Russian headquarters when the grim-faced guard unlocked it. He eyed her suspiciously, then licked his lips, and a sardonic grin spread across his thin, sharp face. There was the smell of rank bacon on his breath, and his thick hair had not yet been combed. Christina was told to wait in the lobby area, and she seated herself on a wooden bench beside the wall as the guard swaggered toward the commandant's office, his heavy footsteps echoing loudly down the stone floor of the corridor.

For three hours, she had waited, watching as the bleak, austere room slowly began to fill with people, mostly old men and old women, mostly in ragged, unwashed clothes. Christina sat amongst them, the hopeless, the condemned, the lost, the damned, and an uneasy feeling settled morosely in the pit of her stomach. Like her, each of them had a request for help, and it troubled her to see the haunted looks on their faces.

There was discontent.

Disillusion.

Disappointment.

And some, obviously, just didn't' care anymore.

An old, white-haired woman, a frayed shawl around her shoulders, turned to Christina and flashed a toothless smile. "These Russians don't treat you right," she said bitterly. "I know. I've been here before."

Christina nodded, but she was in no mood to talk.

"They make you wait," the old woman snapped. "Then they make you beg."

She paused and spit on the floor, wiping her mouth with the back of her hand.

"Then they laugh at you, and they throw you out, and they didn't give you anything."

"Why do you keep coming back?" Christina asked.

The old woman shrugged and tugged at the wrinkles in her black cotton stockings. "I don't have anyplace else to go," she said sadly, leaning back on the bench and closing her eyes with a sigh of mournful resignation.

Christina forced the old woman's bitterness out of her mind. The Russians had never been compassionate people, at least not on occupied soil, she knew. And at times they could indeed be quite exasperating. But, whether anyone liked it or not, Russia held Poland tightly in its huge fist, always squeezing, sometimes crushing those who dared to defy Russian rule. The Polish government, it was written, ran the country. But the Kremlin ran the Polish government.

Christina shifted uncomfortably in her seat. The summer heat had begun to seep into the building, and the stale air was stifling. The lobby area reeked with the odor of rancid sweat and unwashed bodies. For a moment, Christina thought she was going to be sick. Her face felt cold and clammy, and there were chill bumps on her arm. She thought about walking outside for a breath of fresh air to calm her nerves, but she was afraid the guard might call her name, and Christina had no intention of missing her interview with the commandant.

Hers was a simple request.

All she needed was an official exit visa that would allow Christina to be with her husband when he returned home again. That wasn't much to ask. Securing the necessary documents, she had been told by those who were supposed to know, would be a mere formality.

The wait would be the hardest part. Thus far it had been.

Outside, bells atop the old Catholic church across the square were ringing eleven times.

Christina let her mind carry her back to Sopot. She could still taste a hint of the champagne in her mouth, almost hear the violins as they played *In The Mood* and *Symphony of Love* while she danced her first dance as as Mrs. John Christy.

They had checked in to the most exclusive hotel John could find, and a whistling, drunken Captain Andy Anderson carried their bags to the front desk for them.

"We want the two best rooms you have," John told the clerk "One for the captain, and one for the lady and myself.

"I'm afraid that's quite impossible."

John frowned indignantly. "Why?" he blurted out.

"The lady must have a room of her own."

"She's my wife."

The clerk raised a perfectly suspicious eyebrow.

"I'm afraid she's not," he answered. "I can tell by the ring. You're only engaged. This is very reputable hotel, sir, and we simply do not let unmarried men and women share the same room. It's against our policy. I do hope you understand."

"I don't." John's temper was rising.

Christina laughed. "Look at my ring," she told him.

"In Poland, married women wear their wedding rings on their right hand. You placed mine on my left hand."

The captain reached across the desk and grabbed the clerk by his tie. "You want me to hit him, John?" he asked.

"Not yet." John pulled Father Matuszak's marriage certificate from his coat pocket and tossed it to the clerk. He received an apology and two room keys in return.

Even now, Christina wondered if all marriages had such awkward beginnings.

As she waited to see the commandant, it seemed she could still feel the white sand wet beneath her bare feet as she and John walked along the surf line of a midnight beach. It had sparkled in the sunlight. It lay as black velvet in the dim glow of a July moon. The gentle winds brought by the tides of the Baltic Sea had brushed tenderly across her skin as she lay on the crumpled sheets with her husband.

The sunrise, as she knew it must, had taken John away.

"Let me go with you to the ship," Christina had begged as he picked up his bag and started for the door.

"The wharf is a rough place," he said softly. "It's no place for a lady to be, especially by herself. After I'm gone, there would be no one to take care of you down there."

"Then don't go."

"The ship's waiting on me."

A sudden, unexpected fear rushed through Christina. It made her double up with pain. "You will be back, won't you?" Her voice was trembling.

John's laughter was kind, comforting.

"I'm only leaving you for six weeks or so," he said. "As soon as the ship is loaded, we'll be back. And as long as I'm navigating, you can bet that we'll get back faster than we ever have before."

"I'll be waiting for you."

John kissed her, and Christina clung to him, digging her fingernails sharply into his arm.

"I love you," she whispered.

A warm glow had enveloped her. She must see Father Matuszak as soon as she got back to Bgydoszcz, Christina told herself. She had something important to tell him, something important that he needed to know. She loved John Christy. She really did, and there had been times when she was afraid that she would never be capable of loving anyone again.

"I love you," Christina whispered through the open window as she watched John's taxi drive away toward the Baltic Sea and a ship that would take him a thousand miles away from her.

She lay in the bed that smelled of John and cried until noon, and in some ways, Christina never felt better in her life.

She was a woman.

She was a wife.

But, she was alone.

Again.

The thought startled her, and she didn't feel quite so good anymore.

Now Christina's sadness had turned to irritation. The bench had grown hard, and she stood, arms folded, and watched the Russian guards herd people into waiting offices. Sometimes they were out within minutes. Some had been turned away with a mere shake of the head, unable to present their case to any authority. A few had not come back out at all, still trapped on her far side of strong oaken doors that had been strongly locked behind them.

Christina glanced up and saw the Russian guard elbowing his way roughly through the crowd as he approached her. He still wore a sardonic grin, but his hair had been combed. He wiped a trace of spittle from his lips and took Christina by the arm.

"The commandant will see you now," he said. "Maybe I can see you later."

Christina ignored him.

"I can help you get what you want," the guard whispered, "if, of course, you're good to me and give me what I want."

Christina forced a smile, afraid to encourage him, afraid to make him mad.

He winked.

She walked quickly into the commandant's office. The major looked up and raised an eyebrow. He was short and stocky with a round face and ruddy complexion. His uniform was olive, drab, the color, Christina thought, of mildew and mustard. His boots were highly polished, and the graying hair on his temples almost gave him a scholarly look. When the major spoke, he was surly and all business.

"Why are you here?" he asked.

"I have come to apply for an exit visa."

"Why?"

"So I can be with my husband."

"He is not Polish then?"

"No."

"Where is it you want to go?"

"America."

The major looked up and shoved the papers aside on his desk. The acrid smoke from the ashes of his cigar was a veil between them, and his face wrinkled into a chilling smile.

"America?" he asked.

"Yes." Christina sat poised on the edge of the chair, her hands folded neatly in her lap. "My husband is in the American Merchant Marines. We were married two days ago in Bgydoszcz. His ship will be returning to Poland in early September, and I need the exit visa so that I will be able to leave with him."

The Russian Major grunted and sat back in his chair.

The amusement in his eyes died away, and he looked across the desk at Christina with a frown of disapproval.

"I don't recall receiving any notification about your marriage," he said, carefully choosing his words. "I don't recall seeing your request for permission to marry."

Christina swallowed hard. "I'm sure so many come through your office that it's difficult to remember them all," she said.

"Many Polish girls are getting married," he conceded, and sarcasm began to creep into his voice. "But not that many marry an American. I would remember if one requested permission to marry an American."

His laughter was devoid of humor.

It crackled.

Then it abruptly ceased.

"Visa denied," he snapped.

Christina sank back in her chair, fighting off another wave of rage and frustration.

"I don't understand," she said.

"It's simple," the Russian Major answered, his words dripping with insolence. "The fact that you married an American citizen is your business. The fact that you want to leave the country is my business."

He reached for the cigar.

"Visa denied."

"But John is my husband," Christina pleaded.

The major shrugged as if he were no longer interested in her or her plight.

"Then he can live with you in Poland. But you are not allowed to live in America with him."

The commandant turned his back to Christina and dismissed her with a wave of his hand. He had made his ruling, and his decision was final. There was nothing left for him to say.

Christina stumbled from the room, her knees weak and trembling, and shoved her way through a lobby still crowded with nameless people who no longer had faces.

She looked past them, frantic to reach the steps outside, breathing deeply to hide the nausea that was swelling up within her. She felt an arm reach out and grab her.

Christina whirled around and was face to face with the Russian guard. The room began to sway gently beneath her feet, and it smelled of sweat and rank bacon grease. She gagged and broke away, staggering out into the raging glare of bright sunlight that hurt her eyes and made them water.

She heard high-pitched laughing behind her, damning her and mocking her.

Christina looked around and saw the old, white-haired toothless woman standing in the doorway, shaking a bent and bony finger at her, and the laughing grew louder and louder until it became a screech, and Christina held both hands against her ears to shut out the laughter, the noise that cut through the frayed ends of her ragged nerves like a slender, dull-bladed knife.

"They didn't give you nothing, did they?" the old woman yelled.

Christina looked up and down the street, her dark eyes searching wildly for a taxi. There was none.

"They made you wait, then they threw you out, didn't they?" The old woman's laugh had become a cackle.

Christina screamed.

She began running.

"You'll be back," the old woman yelled louder.

Christina felt the heel of her right shoe break, and her knees buckled, but she kept running.

"There's no place else to go."

Christina ran until she was out of sight of the Russian offices and could no longer hear high-pitched laughter behind her. Out of breath, she leaned against a tree, and a bolt of panic, heightened by a nagging fear, shot through her.

John would be coming back for her.

And she would not be allowed to go with him.

She was trapped.

And there was no escape.

He was depending on her.

And she had let him down. She had let them both down.

The old woman was right. There was no place else to go. There was nothing else she could do.

Christina felt like dying. For one agonizing moment, she was as terrified as she had been the morning she climbed among the boxes and crates in the baggage car of Skiorski's train and fled the Berlin border for Poland. As long as there had been hope, Christina didn't mind fighting for what she wanted out of life. Hope had always been able to overshadow her apprehension, her anxieties. Hope had been her strength in the face of any crisis, her light in the darkness, her answered prayer.

Was hope now gone? Nobody ever argued with the Russians and won. They simply arrested you and carted you off, and no one ever saw you again. Christina had heard of the horrors.

Now she didn't know where to turn.

For hours, she walked aimlessly through the streets of Warsaw, knowing she would have to go back to Sophie and Kostek again, ashamed somehow because she had failed.

Christina had a husband.

But it sometimes seemed she no longer had a marriage.

John would settle down in America somewhere, and she would be left to survive as best she could in Poland. A clash of cultures had defeated them, an ocean would separate them. Not even the gold wedding band on her left hand could keep them together when they were worlds apart.

At the railway station, Christina dejectedly took her bag from a locker and walked toward the ticket counter. Her eyes searched the board for a departure time to Bgydoszcz, and they suddenly stopped on the boarding schedule for Sopot.

Maybe the deep voice she had once heard at the other end of a morning telephone could help her, Christina thought. It had been the voice of an American, one that had influence, one that undoubtedly knew how to pull strings and get things done, even when they seemed to be impossible. That's what governmental officials were for, or so they said.

Christina smiled to herself. Hope may be dying, but it wasn't dead yet.

She bought her ticket, and again a night train sped her across the darkness of the Polish countryside. Christina tried to sleep, but it was useless. Come morning and she would be knocking on the door of the American Consulate in Sopot. After all, she owed the honorable Harold Green a visit. He had asked her by telephone to let him know how it all turned out.

Harold Green frowned and replaced his bone china coffee cup on the crystal tray in front of him. He stared across the breakfast table at Christina and shook his head in apparent disbelief. His rich, deep voice was full of understanding and sympathy.

"It hasn't turned out so well, has it," he said.

"I'm afraid not."

Christina had arrived in Sopot about daybreak and taken a small hotel room around the corner from the Consulate. She had showered and washed the tear stains from her face. They were becoming bothersome, Christina thought. There had been so many of them lately. Her eyes were red from lack of sleep, but she hoped the consul wouldn't notice. By nine o'clock she had been knocking on his office door, dressed in the same beige suit and creamy silk blouse that she had worn on her wedding day.

Christina was only eight days away from her twentieth birthday, trying hard to be composed and business-like, even though her insides were a cauldron of boiling emotions. She crossed her long, silky legs as she sipped her black coffee and told Green and his wife, Sylvia, of her years in Budapest, her flight from Hungary, her escape from Berlin, the tragic loss of her parents, and now the fate that was confronting her and her husband.

"Life hasn't been quite fair to you, has it," Green said in his most diplomatic fashion.

Christina smiled sadly but made no effort to reply.

"And now you've come to me for help."

"Yes."

"You will help her, won't you Harold?" Sylvia said.

"I'm not sure what I can do."

"All I need is an exit visa," Christina explained patiently.

"Yes, I know." Green rubbed his chin, deep in his own thoughts. He was dressed as always in a three piece, pin-stripe suit, even during the dog days of summer. His tie and socks were silk, and his shoes were designed of the finest Italian leather. He was a man of visible affluence, and he was not hesitant at all about surrounding himself with the pleasures that his money had bought and paid for. Green didn't flaunt his good fortune or his wealth. He simply enjoyed it to the hilt. He and Sylvia lived and officed in a luxurious villa that had once been owned by a Jewish surgeon who, during the war, had disappeared. The consul had no intention of letting his manor, overlooking the Baltic Sea, go to waste. A chauffeur drove him and his wife around town, and servants quickly answered the snap of every finger.

It didn't surprise Harold Green that such a gentile and lovely young creature had come asking him for help during her time of trouble. He was the obvious one to assist her. After all, he himself had played a small role in getting John Christy and Christina together in the first place.

Green turned his full attention again to Christina and smiled his most appropriate diplomatic smile. "I'm not really for sure what I can do," he said.

Christina wavered slightly.

"Harold," Sylvia interrupted, "all she needs is an exit visa. Surely you can get her one of those."

"It's not that easy," he replied. "The Russians have access to all the legal exit visas. They decide who comes into Poland and who leaves. Unfortunately, I have no say so in those affairs at all."

Sylvia poured herself another glass of orange juice, laced heavily with Russian vodka. It was, she said privately, the only thing from the Kremlin worth having.

Sylvia Green had been described by men and women alike as usually beautiful and always elegant. She made it a point to wear the latest fashions from Paris or London, and no one had ever seen Sylvia unless her makeup was perfect and her long nails manicured. Her dark hair fell in a gentle wave upon her shoulders. Sylvia, day or night, looked at the world around her through striking green eyes that were not always in focus. She loved her husband. She loved his job. She detested his duty in Sopot.

"Is there anything that can be done?" Christina asked, fighting desperately to suppress the fear that kept churning without mercy in her stomach.

Green laughed and patted her hand reassuringly. "There's always something that can be done. Unfortunately, it can never be done overnight," he said. "All of this governmental red tape ties us up rather tightly sometimes, I'm afraid, and it takes a while to get the knots sorted out. In the meantime, I'll check around with a few American consuls in other countries and try to determine just which might be the best course for us to follow."

"When should you know something?" Christina asked, trying hard to quell the tremor in her voice.

"Perhaps by later today."

Green looked at his watch, then at his wife. She was refilling her glass with orange juice, and his deep-set eyes registered their disapproval. He turned again to Christina and forced a smile.

"Why don't you and Sylvia spend some time together this afternoon while I call around," he said. "She gets rather lonely here, and I'm sure she would enjoy your company."

"Harold tells everyone I'm bored," his wife said.

She held her orange juice up toward the sun and let its reflections cut through the prism of the glass.

"He's just being nice," she continued.

Sylvia reached under the table, pulled out a half empty bottle of vodka, and began to slowly unscrew the cap.

"He's only worried about me because he thinks I drink too much." Sylvia shrugged sadly and admitted the truth to them all. "I do drink too much." She closed her eyes, took a deep breath and exhaled. It was an abrupt, exasperated sound. "I might as well. There's nothing else to do around here except go stark, raving mad."

Green was suddenly very uncomfortable. He prided himself in the fact that he never perspired, not even during summer, not even when wearing a three piece suit when the sun was hot overhead. But now tiny beads of sweat had seeped into the creases of his face. "I do wish you would remain as our guest awhile," he said to Christina.

Christina glanced awkwardly at Sylvia Green, not really sure if she would be welcome.

"Please stay," Sylvia said, and her smile was sincere. "It's quite nice to hear someone other than Harold speaking English around this place. The servants speak Polish. My chauffeur speaks Polish. Everybody in Sopot speaks Polish." She shrugged and finished off her glass of orange juice, motioning for Christina to follow her out into the garden. "I don't like Polish."

"Why?" Christina looked puzzled.

"Because I can't understand a word of it." Sylvia began laughing, and Christina laughed with her.

It was late in the day, and the lengthening shadows had almost bedded down the roses and sunflowers when Harold Gray came to them in the garden.

Christina looked at him expectantly, eager to hear what he had to tell her, afraid of what his words might be.

"There is a way for you to leave Poland and be with John," he announced.

Christina's face brightened.

"But it may take some time."

The brightness faded.

"John can start the ball rolling for you when he gets back to America," the consul said. "Since you are his wife, he can initiate proceedings with the immigration department, and its authorities can prepare the proper documents you need to travel to the United States. It's simple, really, but it's a lengthy process, and the red tape tends to get a bit sticky, particularly between our country and the Russians. I'm afraid you can't find a whole lot of trust on either side."

"How long will it take?" Christina's voice was that of a child.

"No one can be for sure," Green replied. "Bureaucracy has its own time frame, and it's usually out of sync with the rest of the world." He shrugged jovially. "But who knows? With a little luck, you may be out of here and home by Christmas."

"But that's four months away," Christina protested.

"I'm sorry."

"It's not fair."

"It's the best I can do." Green paused and shoved his hands into his coat pocket. He lowered his voice. "There's only one other solution I can offer you," he said.

"What's that?"

"If you can find a way, any way, to get back to Berlin, the American military will put on a troop transport ship bound for the United States."

"The Russians won't allow me to return to Berlin," Christina said.

"You smuggled yourself out of Germany." Green sighed. "You might just have to smuggle yourself back in again."

Christina caught her breath.

She broke out in a cold sweat.

For a moment, in her mind, she was reliving the terror of lying in the darkness of a baggage car, listening while Russian guards, armed with submachine guns, harshly announced their plans to search the train, knowing she would be arrested or shot down on the spot if they discovered her.

She loved John.

But she was not strong enough to face the Russians and the threat of death again.

Christina was now confronted with two options, and neither was acceptable to her. She walked away from the consul and looked out across the Baltic Sea as it turned to purple in the fading light of day.

She felt empty.

And alone.

Always alone.

When Green had left, Sylvia reached for her bottle of vodka, held it out to Christina, and asked, "Do you want a drink now?"

Christina hesitated. "I don't like vodka," she said.

"You don't drink vodka because you like it," Sylvia replied, her words beginning to slur. "You drink it when you're upset and frustrated and have your back to the wall and can't find a way out."

She poured a jigger full into a demitasse cup and handed it to Christina.

Night had begun to roll from out of the sea and touch the shoreline of Sopot. The evening star dangled low in the horizon, mocking Christina with its brightness. She had wished upon it so many times during the past nineteen, almost twenty, years. It had betrayed her. The same star that looked down upon her was also looking down on Russia, and she silent cursed them both.

Christina took a sip from the cup and felt the vodka burn her throat. She made a face, then said to no one in particular, "I wish I were a bird."

Sylvia's laugh had a hollow sound.

Christina pointed toward the seagulls that had caught the crest of an evening wind and were soaring gently above the sands of Sopot's beach.

"I wish I were a bird," she repeated. "Then I could fly away and all of my problems would be over."

"Don't give up hope," Sylvia encouraged her.

"There's none left. The Russians have destroyed it. It's as though, they purposely took all of the hope they could find, then trampled on it with their heavy boots and crushed it beneath their feet."

"Where there's a will, there's a way."

"In America, maybe, but not in Poland."

A mischievous gleam caught in Sylvia's eye. "I know what I would do if I were in your shoes," she said.

"What?"

"I'd stow away on John's ship."

Christina was dumbfounded. "I don't understand," she said, taking anther sip of vodka and holding it in her mouth.

"About what?"

"What do you mean by stow away?"

Sylvia curdled her orange juice again with vodka and replied slowly, "I mean you should sneak aboard John's ship the night before it leaves for America and hide away when there's nobody looking."

"But what happens if he finds me?"

"Oh, he'll find you all right."

"But what will they do to me?"

"Well," Sylvia slurred, "they sure as hell won't throw you back, not when they're that far out at sea. And they sure as hell won't take the time to bring you back here. The only choice they have left is to pack you up and take you on to America with them."

Christina adamantly shook her hand. "That's a crazy idea," she said. "It's out of the question."

"Others have done it."

"What happened to them?"

"Most of them made it."

Christina finished her vodka without even tasting it. "I could never get away with it."

"It's a risk," Sylvia admitted.

"No." Christina had made up her mind. "I can't do it."

"Do you really love John?"

"Yes."

"Well," Sylvia sighed. "I'd do the impossible to be with the man I loved."

"John might get mad."

"Probably."

"He might not ever forgive me."

"He will if he loves you."

"I'm afraid."

Sylvia shrugged. "I'd much rather face the Americans than the Russians," she replied. "At least they won't shoot you." Her laugh, like her orange juice, was heavily laced with vodka.

Chapter 16

CHRISTINA CHRISTY LOOKED AGAIN at the wedding gifts she had spread out on the bed before her. They were barely visible in the dim light of early morning, and she handled each one with care and with love. They were old, crystal and china and fine linen that had sometimes been passed down for generations, family heirlooms that meant as much to the givers as to Christina herself. In Poland, no one ever went out and bought a new gift for a bride on her wedding day. That would be a disgrace. That would be an insult. Gifts came from the heart, from the array of antiques that people had collected through the years: a bowl that mother had used, a scarf that grandmother had worn, a churn that had made the butter for their table when all of them were children so long ago. Each gift had a meaning, a history, an importance all of its own.

Christina realized that she was sitting amidst an inheritance that had been gathered especially for her, and for her alone. It was something special. It was tradition.

She wept.

Christina gingerly set the last bowl aside and knew that she would never see any of the gifts again.

Slowly she dressed as the September sun outside began its morning climb into the sky. The chill of early autumn had spread across Poland, and Christina packed an extra sweater. She might need it before she got home.

She looked around the room and the harsh, cold reality of the daring covenant that Christina had made with herself suddenly struck her with the impact of a rifle shot.

This was home.

This would never be home again.

For the past six weeks, Christina had watched time crawl past her. At first, she counted the days until she would see John again, then she threw the calendar away. The days were too long, the hours moved so slowly that she was sometimes convinced the minute hand had abandoned its place on the face of the hallway clock. The whole month of August, she believed, was destined to last forever. And the waiting was a torture that grated against her nerves and gradually left Christina drowning in the murky depths of her own impatience.

Her first couple of weeks back in Bgydoszcz had been frustrating, but not particularly unbearable. To many in the neighborhood, Christina had become something of a celebrity. After all, she had married a handsome American sailor, an officer even, and she had openly and successfully defied the Russian authorities, saying her sacred wedding vows virtually within hearing distance of the Red Army patrols that looked down like vultures upon the town.

"When are you going to America?" neighbors kept asking her.

"Soon, I hope," she kept answering.

In her nightmares, Christina could not flee the stern, unforgiving face of the Russian major in Warsaw, and she was forever being awakened at night to the howl of laughter that had trailed after her as she ran, never quite outdistancing that toothless smile or the smell of rancid bacon grease that made her feel vile and unclean.

Christina walked among the gardens of Bgydoszcz. She attended mass every other day. She laughed with her Uncle Kostek. She had long conversations with Father Matsuzak. But she kept her horrible secret to herself. Only Sophie knew that the Russian major had turned down her request for an exit visa. Only Sophie knew that Christina was stranded in her own homeland. But no one knew what she was contemplating.

Christina had not been able to force Sylvia's words from her mind or forget them. They intrigued her. They became an obsession.

It was ridiculous to even think about stowing away on John's ship, she told herself.

It's foolish not to consider it, she answered back.

At the moment, Christina Christy had no other choice.

On the morning of September 6, Christina took one last longing look at her wedding presents, picked up her bag, quietly closed the door behind her, and walked into the room where Aunt Sophie was waiting for her.

The older woman had been crying, but now she was putting up a brave front, although her eyes betrayed her.

"I'll miss you, Krischia," she said.

"I love you, too," Christina answered.

Sophie stroked her niece's curls in silence for a few minutes, then said softly, "It's hard on me to see you go, Krischia."

"I understand." Christina's felt herself being pulled between two worlds. Her heart was aching for John. It was breaking for Sophie.

"You were gone so long. I didn't think I would ever see you again. Then you came home. And now you're going again."

Her smile was a sad one.

It matched the one Christina was wearing.

"What happens if the American consul can't get you out of a German port?" Sophie asked.

Her aunt only knew what Christina had told her, and Christina had kept most of the truth to herself.

"I'm going to spend as much time as possible with John." she replied. "And if things don't work out right for me, I'll be back."

Sophie stared deep into Christina's nervous eyes. "I don't think you're coming back," she said. "You want to be with John. So you'll find a way." Sophie shrugged in a motherly sort of way. "You're a Skiba, Krischia. Skibas always find a way. It's in your blood."

"I won't ever give up trying." Christina wrapped a pink woolen sweater around her shoulders. It hung loosely over her white ruffled blouse and black skirt.

"I hope you're happy," Sophie said hoarsely.

"I'll write you." Her words seemed so meaningless, so hollow, but Christina could think of nothing else to say.

Sophie slipped a gold bracelet from her arm and handed it to Christina. "It belonged to your grandmother," she said. "Now it belongs to you. Maybe someday, you will have a little girl, and then it will belong to her."

Christina hugged her aunt.

"Whatever you do," Sophie whispered, "don't ever lose your identity. Be proud of your heritage, and don't let anyone force you to change your values of life. They are your greatest asset. They are what's important to you, here, or in America, or wherever you go."

Christina tried to speak, but the tears she had swallowed would not let her. She squeezed Sophie's hand, kissed it, and ran out of the room. Kostek was waiting outside beside the taxi. If Christina's train were on time, he figured that she had an hour to reach the station, and Kostek watched sadly as the taxi pulled out quickly into the midmorning traffic.

The train was late.

Christina had separated herself from the crowd and was standing on the platform outside, her back against the wall, when she saw the gypsy woman weaving through the tangled mass of humanity. Her gold earrings caught the glint of the overhead sun, and the woman's stringy black hair was partially hidden by a faded, flowery scarf. Her silk purple blouse still hadn't been washed, and the aging gypsy plodded toward Christina on bare feet.

Her black eyes were searing.

The smile on her face caused Christina to shudder, then look quickly away.

The gypsy was laughing, but she made no sound, and, as if as by magic, a deck of dirty playing cards unexpectedly appeared in the long, skinny fingers of her right hand.

"You ignored me once," she whispered harshly. "You can't afford to ignore me again. There is too much sadness in your life, too much uncertainty in your eyes."

"Go away."

The gypsy slowly began to turn the torn cards, one at a time.

"Leave me alone."

She pulled a queen of hearts from the deck and held it close to Christina's face.

"What you are going to do is very dangerous," the gypsy whispered. "Will it work out for you?" Her face became serious, and the soiled queen of hearts disappeared from her hand. "For twenty-five *zlotys*, I will tell your fortune."

Christina hesitated.

She was afraid of gypsies or anyone who could look into the future. She was afraid of what they knew. She was afraid of what she didn't know. Christina opened her black oversize leather purse and counted out twenty-five *zlotys.*

The gypsy woman sat down on the platform and spread the cards out before her. "A tall, handsome man is in your life, and he is madly in love with you. Is that right?"

Christina nodded.

"Soon you will cross a huge pond."

The gypsy frowned and her hands began to tremble.

"You will encounter anger and tears and confusion," she continued. "Much anger. Many tears. Much confusion. But the outcome . . ." the gypsy paused and began to gather up her cards, putting them back into the pocket of her striped skirt.

"What about the outcome?"

The gypsy shrugged as she rose to her feet. "It will be the way you want it to be," she said, and she disappeared into the crowd that was pushing its way down toward the edge of the tracks. The abrupt whistle of the approaching locomotive erupted around them, and Christina, somewhat perplexed and puzzled by what the fortune teller had told her, found herself being pushed along in the mad rush to board the train.

From her room in the Hotel Internationale in Sopot, Christina placed a late afternoon call to the villa of the American consul. She told the maid who answered that she wished to speak to Sylvia Green, then waited. After a long while, she heard Sylvia's voice, thick with vodka, stammer a hesitant hello on the other end of the line.

"This is Christina," she said.

There was a squeal of delight.

"John's ship is arriving tomorrow morning."

"Well, my dear," Sylvia inquired, regaining her composure. "Have you decided what you're going to do yet?"

"I need to talk to you."

Sylvia's laughter was deep and throaty. "That takes the mystery out of it then," she said. "I guess you've finally made up your mind." Sylvia paused a moment, then asked, "You want to meet at the villa or at the hotel?"

"Here, if you don't mind."

"Where?"

"In the bar."

Sylvia laughed again. "I just hope the bartender has enough vodka to help us both make it through the night. I'll see you in thirty minutes."

She hung up.

Christina had already finished two glasses of wine by the time Sylvia came walking into the darkness of the bar. The consul's wife was dressed elegantly, as usual. Her hair had been pulled up into a knot on top of her head, and her dress was so blue that it was almost the color of midnight. The fur draped around her shoulders was definitely Russian and definitely expensive. Sylvia never flaunted her wealth. It was just that the day was chilly, and she wore whatever she could find in the closet to keep the cold wind off her shoulders.

She took Christina's hand, laughed loud, too loud probably, and said, "I'm glad to see you again."

The two women chatted pleasantly, eager to catch up on what had happened to each of them during the past six weeks. Sylvia had ordered her second vodka martini before she finally said, "So you've decided to go with John."

Christina sighed. "It's still a crazy idea, isn't it?"

"Most good ideas are." Sylvia pulled her chair closer to Christina and asked confidentially, "Have you told anyone?"

"No. Of course not."

"Not even your aunt?"

"Nobody knows."

"How about your priest?"

"I'm afraid I lied to him, too."

"Good." Sylvia breathed easier. She leaned back and asked calmly, "Now, how are you going to do it?"

"I have no idea." Christina giggled. The wine had begun to tease her. "That's why I wanted to talk to you. What the hell do I do?" Her language was out of character, and she giggled again.

Sylvia thought for a moment. "What kind of ship does John have?"

"I don't know. He's never let me see it."

"Getting aboard is the tough part." Sylvia ordered another martini. "There will be armed Polish guards out on the gangplank, and they don't let anyone on ship who hasn't been authorized." Then she grinned. "But don't worry. I'll just get you a pass from the consul."

"Can you do that?"

"I can unless Harold wants to sleep alone the rest of the winter, and it gets cold as hell about December." Sylvia snapped her fingers. "I've got a better idea," she said. "Just make sure that the captain invites you on board for dinner the night before the ship sails. John himself can escort you past the Polish guards."

"The captain may not let me come aboard."

"He's got to. You're the wife of one of his executive officers, and you're curious about where your husband lives when he's at sea for such long periods of time. Besides, you told me that that the captain served as best man for your wedding. Inviting you for dinner is the least he can do."

"Maybe John will object."

Sylvia winked. "You've got a full night with John to change his mind, and if you're any woman at all, that should be the easiest thing you've ever done."

Christina blushed. "I may not know how," she said softly.

"Just do what comes naturally, and you'll have John eating out of your hand for the rest of his life." Sylvia's amusement died away, and her tone abruptly changed. "Once you get on board," she warned, "stay on board."

"How do I do that?"

"After dinner, just take a casual stroll around the deck. Find yourself a good hiding place and disappear."

"What about John?"

"Don't breathe a word of your plan to John. He can't help you at all. If he did, and if he got caught, it would severely damage his career, maybe even ruin it."

Christina grew silent.

Suddenly, she didn't like the idea at all. Christina didn't mind risks. She had taken them before. But John's future might be at stake, and she didn't want to do anything that would jeopardize him. Too much wine was making her head light and fluffy, and it was filling her mind with quizzical, absurd thoughts that kept getting tangled up together, and she was having a hard time making sense out of any of them.

Christina was tired.

So tired.

She wanted to sleep.

And she wanted to wake up with John's arms around her and live happily forever after like they always did in fairy tales. Christina loved fairy tales. She always had.

In fairy tales, nobody ever kept a secret.

And now she had to keep a secret.

John mustn't know.

John mustn't suspect anything.

Now she would have to lie to John, and she had promised that she would never lie to him.

Christina lay her head on the table and wished she were a little girl again, snuggled beneath the quilts of her own bed, waiting for her mother to come and kiss her goodnight.

Why did she have to grow up?

Growing up was such a hard, depressing thing to do.

Christina opened one eye and stared through the fog at Sylvia. "Will you help me?" she asked in a childish voice.

The consul's wife smiled sympathetically and patted Christina's shoulder. "I'll give you your instructions," she replied, "But then you need to practice every move in your head as though you were rehearsing for a play. I'll write the script, but the actual performance is up to you."

Christina let out a long breath. Somehow, that's how she knew it would be.

Common sense told her that she should just wait and let John have the proper documents prepared for her in the United States. But Harold Green had checked further, and he had told her weeks ago, "I'm afraid it could take as much as a year, possibly even eighteen months, before you would be allowed to enter the United States."

"I can't wait that long."

"I'm afraid you don't have a lot of alternatives."

But she did.

Then the letter came from John, full of hope and full of love. "I know by now your traveling papers are in order," he had written. "It won't be long until we can at last be together and stay together and return to America together."

That's what John wanted.

That's what she would do for him.

Chapter 17

JOHN CHRISTY SAT ON THE EDGE OF HIS hotel bed and stared down at Christina in total dismay and disbelief. For six weeks, he had been making preparations to have her return with him, and now she was telling him she couldn't go. Disgust registered on his face, then rage. The Russians had no right to interfere with his life, with his happiness. There was no reason at all for Christina to be caught, trapped in a web of dispassionate red tape where she was not looked upon as a person, only as a number. John trembled with anger. His jaws tightened. He slammed a fist into the pillow that lay wadded up beside him.

For a moment, Christina looked upon a face she had never seen before, and it frightened her.

"I'm sorry," she whispered, and the tears came.

"I'm not blaming you." John's eyes softened. "I just don't understand why the Russians think it's so damned important to keep you in Poland. It doesn't make sense."

"Nothing the Russians ever do makes sense."

"I've missed you so much Christina." Disappointment seeped into John's voice. "And just when I thought I would have you forever, I find out that I'm losing you again."

Christina ran her fingertips across his naked back and watched as the reflection of a setting sun burnished his face a golden tan.

"I'll get you out of here some way," John said, pulling her closer to him. "I don't know how. I don't know how long it will take. But I'll get the best damn lawyer I can find back in Virginia, and together we'll figure out a way to pry you loose from the Russians. In the meantime, I'll check with the American consul here and see what strings he can pull."

"I've already talked to him."

"What did he tell you?"

"That you would have to begin proceedings with the Immigration Department back in the United States."

"Then that's where I'll start. How long did he think it would take?"

"A year, maybe. Possibly even eighteen months."

"Damn."

John slammed his fist into the pillow again, harder this time.

"There's got to be a better way," he snapped.

Yes, there is, Christina wanted to tell him. I'll be going with you when you leave. Please understand. And please forgive me. The words lodged in her throat, but Christina could not speak them. She smiled instead and reached up her arms to embrace John, nestling her head against his chest, closing her eyes to shut out the reality that had ensnared them both.

John had promised to take her dancing.

Maybe, just maybe, the band would play *In the Mood* and *Symphony of Love* again.

But not now.

Now she needed simply to be alone with John. She could dance later.

Christina had a night to convince John that he needed to take her aboard ship for dinner on his last evening in Sopot. That's what Sylvia had said. Christina smiled to herself as she felt John's strong arms wrap around her and hold her tightly. If she were any kind of woman at all, one night was all it would take. Sometimes Christina could be any kind of woman she wanted to be.

She didn't dance at all that night.

All afternoon, Christina had tried hard to act as dejected and melancholy as John felt. In reality, she was scared to death. Her moment of truth was now only hours away, and she wondered if she were courageous enough, strong enough to go through with her plan. John, all through the day, had put up a brave front, although Christina could sense the depression settling down heavy upon his shoulders. As far as he knew, this would be their last night together for a long time. John's ship was not scheduled to bring him back to Poland anytime in the near future, and Christina, for all practical purposes, found herself locked securely away in a Russian prison without bars. She was free. Yet, in Poland, she would never be free.

John had left the hotel at five o'clock. "I'll be back in an hour," he promised. "Dinner will be served promptly at seven. And I'm sure Andy is planning some sort of farewell party for us."

He tried to smile.

Christina kissed him.

Then she sat alone, her stomach knotted with fear. The gypsy had said everything would turn out all right, or at least the way Christina wanted it to be. But gypsies lied, and Christina knew all about lying. For the last three days, she had kept the truth from John, watching his spirit slowly disintegrate as his time for departure grew nearer.

Christina picked up the telephone, wanting to talk to Sylvia one last time, wanting to hear her final words of encouragement before she knowingly and willingly broke the law in the sight of man, but not in the sight of God. Christina held the phone in her lap until the room began to grow dark as the sun hid its face behind a thunderhead in the west, then she placed the receiver back on its hook. Before John's ship docked, she and Sylvia had decided that it would probably be unwise for them to see each other or even talk to each other again. Neither wanted to arouse suspicions, and Sylvia could not afford to be linked with Christina's actions in any way. Her husband's job, too, might be at stake.

Christina glanced at the clock outside her hotel window. She had thirty minutes left before she heard John's knock. That wasn't much time, but Christina had memorized everything she must do. She removed her negligee and began to get ready for her long voyage at sea.

Christina dressed in her beige wedding suit, wearing a navy blue wool sweater beneath it instead of a blouse. She slipped on a pair of low-heeled suede Italian shoes, then packed her oversized leather purse with an extra sweater, nylons, underwear, toothbrush, makeup, jewelry, and passport. That was all she could afford to carry with her. The rest of her clothes would be left behind.

She glanced in the mirror and wondered how John could love anyone who looked so pale and fragile. There were dark circles under her eyes, and her olive skin was waxen, the color of alabaster.

The knock at the door startled her.

She looked again at the clock and sighed. John, as always, was right on time. She sighed again. It was now or never.

Christina opened the door, her knees weak and trembling. The strain had contorted her face and she tried, without any success, to release the tension that gripped her with a smile. She appeared more shaken than John had ever seen her before.

"Are you feeling all right?" he asked.

Christina nodded. "I'm just a little nervous," she replied. "I can't help it."

"I have some bad news," John said.

"What could get any worse?"

"I'll be standing watch on deck from eight o'clock until midnight," John answered. "After dinner, I won't have time to show you around the ship. Nobody will. This is not really a good time at all for you to come aboard."

"I don't mind," Christina said softly. "Really I don't. It's just so important to me to see where you work and live. That's a memory I can keep with me after you've gone." She took his hand. "While you're on watch, I'll just look around the ship until I get bored, then I'll catch a taxi back to the hotel and wait for you."

"I'll be there as soon as I get off duty."

Christina's kiss lightly brushed his cheek. "I know you will," she whispered.

Arm in arm, they walked down the hallway and out into the frosty evening air. The clouds had grown thick above them, and a bitter wind came boiling off the Baltic Sea. Christina snuggled her face against the warmth of John's shoulder as they shielded each other from an autumn mist that swirled down madly around them.

The taxi ride from Sopot to the port of Gdansk took them thirty minutes. Within that distance, the complexion of the coast began to change drastically. John had been right, Christina told herself. The dock area was a rough, dirty, niggardly place to be, much like the men with sordid faces and dishonest eyes who hung around the wharf and its warehouses. It was definitely no place for a lady.

"Be careful when you leave tonight," John warned.

"Don't worry about me."

"I love you."

"I'll be fine."

"Stay with the guards until your taxi arrives."

Christina smiled. She didn't answer.

John waved at the Polish guards as he and Christina approached the gangplank.

"You are not allowed to smuggle a pretty girl on board ship," one of them said with broken English as he laughed.

"She's my wife."

"That's what they all say."

"I can prove it."

"That's what they all say." The guard laughed again.

John produced a pass that Captain Anderson had signed, then slipped each man a couple of packs of American cigarettes, and the guard smiled his gratitude as he motioned them both aboard. Cigarettes were still hard to get in Poland. They were expensive. Some men would sell their soul or their mother for an American cigarette. John never went anywhere without a few extra packs in his pocket. He never knew when or where he might need them. They were more valuable than money.

The sight of the ship had taken Christina's breath away. It was huge, much larger than she could have ever imagined, rising up like a great metal building from the sea. It was both intimidating and reassuring. Surely, somewhere within the darkened bowels of such a massive vessel, there would be a hiding place for Christina.

During the few spare minutes they had before dinner, John escorted her to his quarters.

"Your room is so neat and clean," Christina remarked, then shrugged. "You are a much better housekeeper than I am, John. I can't cook. I can't sew. I've never washed a load of clothes. I've never even ironed a shirt. I'm afraid you'll find me useless around a house."

"Willie, the Chinese cabin boy, does it all for me. He takes care of all the deck officers."

"Good." Christina laughed. "You can bring Willie, the Chinese cabin boy, home with you when you come."

"I can't."

"Why not?"

"He's the captain's pet."

"Then bring the captain home, too."

Andy was waiting for her when Christina was ushered into officer's mess. He hugged her without ceremony and whispered, "I'm sorry things haven't worked out for you and John."

She squeezed his arm and smiled in reply.

"Just don't ever give up hope."

"I never have before."

"No, you haven't." Andy held Christina's chair for her. "I guess I'll have to call you chicken," he said.

"Why?" Christina looked puzzled.

"Well, where I come from, a chicken is a coward," Andy replied. "And Lord knows you're not a coward. You're just about the bravest little girl I've ever known."

Christina shook her head, not really comprehending what Andy had told her. "Is that what you call American logic?" she questioned.

Andy grinned, then broke into laughter.

"That's American humor," John said.

"I don't understand it."

"It's a compliment."

"Then I like it." Christina gave Andy a quick kiss before she sat down.

Only two other officers were sitting with them.

"We're operating with a skeleton crew tonight," Andy explained. "Since this is our last night in port, everyone who is not on duty has shore leave. It's their last chance to live it up and raise a little hell for a long time. It'll be seventeen long, tedious days before they have solid ground beneath their feet again." He paused, poured himself a cup of coffee, then looked apologetically at Christina. "That's why John has to stand watch until midnight. I know it's not fair to you, but we all have to do what we have to do, and I've sworn to do my best to treat every man on board as fairly as I can. I just don't make exceptions, Christina, for myself, for John, for anyone."

"I understand."

Andy lifted his cup in a toast. "To the newlyweds," he said loudly. "I helped you tie the knot, but it must have been a slip knot, because I have never seen anybody have as much trouble getting together and staying together as you two have. Good luck, and I mean that sincerely."

Thanks Andy, Christina whispered under her breath. Before the night is over, I'll be needing all the luck I can get.

By the time Christina finished her steak and downed her last cup of coffee, the officers had eaten and were gone, leaving her and John by themselves.

He stood and took a deep, mournful breath. "It's time for me to go now," he said.

Christina's nerves were ragged and raging inside her like a winter gale.

He reached down and kissed her forehead. "Have a good time while you're on the ship," John continued. "I'll see you back at the hotel as soon after midnight as I can get there."

Poor John, Christina thought. He'll be so worried. He'll look for me, and I won't be there. I won't be anywhere where he can find me.

"I love you, John," was all she said.

Christina watched him walk tall and proud out of the room.

The next time she saw John, it would be under adverse circumstances. He would be angry. But he would be near her, and that's all that mattered anymore.

She quickly picked up a handful of crackers from a basket on the table and stuffed them into her purse. She had no idea when she would eat again.

Christina squared her shoulders, gathered up what courage she could muster, and slipped quietly out into the chilled darkness of the night.

For thirty minutes—it seemed longer—she wandered aimlessly down one corridor, then another. In the distance, Christina heard the faint sounds of talk and laughter as the noise drifted with the wind on toward the stern of the ship. The mist had quit falling, and there were scattered breaks in the clouds. They did not appear nearly as threatening as they had earlier in the evening.

Christina stopped and shivered.

At her feet she saw the edge of a black hole, partially concealed by a metallic cover that some sailor had carelessly left open and apparently forgotten. Kneeling, Christina examined it more closely. A thin shaft of moonlight threaded its way into the interior of the hole, and she thought she could make out the rough outlines of burlap bags piled on the floor. They didn't look to be too deep, and Christina decided there was no use to search any further nor wait any longer.

She glanced around her.

The deck was empty.

Her heart was pounding fiercely as Christina began to lower herself slowly and methodically into the hole. Her feet dangled for a moment or two, then she lost her grip and fell off balance into a pit much blacker and deeper than she had thought. Her face slammed against an iron rod protruding from the wall, and a bolt of unbearable pain shot through her head. Christina could hear the unmistakable sound of her own flesh tearing as she plunged to the bottom of a paint storage shed. A jagged burst of light flashed across her eyes as though they had been ripped apart by a stroke of angry lightning. Christina felt herself go limp, and she crumpled upon the burlap like a rag doll that had been thoughtlessly thrown away.

She lay in the darkness terrified. The pain was sharp and piercing, and she felt her face grow wet, then cold. Christina touched her forehead, and it was moist and sticky, and she could taste the salt from her own sweat and blood.

A wave of nausea swept over her. Christina tried to move but couldn't, and she lay face down, suffocating in the burlap, wracked by convulsions.

Dear God, she asked silently, am I going to die?

Why me?

Why now?

Before He answered, Christina lost consciousness and couldn't feel the hurt anymore.

Chapter 18

JOHN CHRISTY WAS OUT OF BREATH. He raced down a back alley behind the docks of Gdansk, frantically searching every shadow for some trace of Christina, afraid he would find her, afraid he would not. He leaned against the soiled bricks of an old abandoned warehouse as he reached the street again, sweat creasing his worried face. John no longer felt the cold of the night.

He checked his watch. It was four o'clock.

Christina had simply vanished off the face of the earth.

John had turned his duty over to a junior officer shortly after midnight, hurriedly changed from his khaki work uniform, and sped as quickly as the taxi would carry him back to the Hotel Internationale in Sopot. He knew he would have eight hours left to spend with Christina before his ship departed. He knew she would be waiting for him.

John had knocked repeatedly and loudly on the door, and there had been no answer.

He had used his own key to enter the room. It was empty.

Christina was gone.

Her clothes still hung in the closet. Her suitcase was packed and had been shoved into the corner. In fact, the room looked just as it had the last time John was there.

It smelled of Christina's perfume.

But there were no signs that she had returned from the ship at all.

"I have not seen her since she left earlier this evening with you," the concierge told him. "She has not come back to the hotel. I still have her key."

John walked briskly into the bar.

Three women were seated beside the bandstand. Another sat alone in the corner.

Neither of them was Christina.

Growing impatient, John had called the American consul. No, Harold Green told him, Christina wasn't there. In fact, it had been weeks since either he or his wife had heard from her. But if she did telephone, he would certainly tell her that John was looking for her.

For an hour, John Christy ran up one street, then down another, checking every bar and cabaret he found, first in Sopot, then in Gdansk. No lady matching Christina's description had been seen in any of them.

Fear trailed his footsteps.

John could feel it. He could almost smell it.

Christina had not really acted like herself that evening, he remembered. Her moods had kept changing. She was happy one minute and sad the next, talkative, then silent, full of laughter, full of tears. He hadn't really understood her, but then he seldom did. She was totally unpredictable, and maybe that's why he loved her so.

At first, John thought that, perhaps, his wife had simply been wandering the street, caught up in her own loneliness. She had lost track of time. That was all.

Now he just didn't know anymore.

Surely she hadn't run away.

Christina had been upset. John knew that. He had been upset, too.

But that was no reason for her to run away.

They had still had eight hours left to be together.

It was almost daylight when John dragged himself back to the ship. He looked back over the skyline of Gdansk, a faint silhouette against the dawn, and cursed himself for ever being born.

Christina was his love, his wife.

What had happened to her?

Where had she gone?

John found Captain Anderson on the bridge. Andy yelled at him, "What the hell are you doing back so early? Surely the honeymoon's not over with this quickly."

John didn't answer.

He slumped into a chair, and Andy saw the pallid, ashen face of a beaten man in the harsh glow of his overhead light. "Damn, John," he said, "what's the matter? You look like a dead man."

"It's Christina."

"What about her?"

"I can't find her."

"What happened?"

"I don't know."

Panic surfaced in John's eyes. He lay his head back against the wall and stared at the ceiling. His shoulders sagged, and the creases deepened in his face.

"She's got to be some place."

"I don't know where else to look."

A tear fought its way out of the corner of John's eyes and rolled down his stoic face.

"You've got to find her," Andy said adamantly.

"It's too late." John shrugged wearily. "She's gone.

She's run away, and she doesn't belong to me anymore. It's as if she never existed at all."

John stood and shuffled down the hallway to his quarters, falling into his bunk without bothering to undress. He was young. He had a whole lifetime to live. But for the first time, John Christy knew that he had begun to die.

When she awoke, Christina could feel the ship moving. She looked up and saw a tiny sliver of daylight darting down between a crack in the deck floor above her. Sometime during the night, someone had fit the metal cover back in its place, and Christina wondered if she were locked in the hole. If so, would anyone find her, or would she simply lay there upon her bed of burlap and slowly starve to death.

Her head still throbbed, although the sharp pain had become nothing more than a dull ache. To Christina it felt like someone was pounding a nine-pound hammer against her temples. Without mercy. Without pity. Without ceasing. The bleeding had stopped, but her left eye was swollen and closed, and the nausea was coming back.

Above her, Christina could hear men running back and forth, and distorted voices were shouting orders, sometimes near and sometimes far away, and the ship began to gently sway in the water. Christina painfully pulled herself into an upright position and reached for the pack of crackers that had spilled from her purse. She was hidden. She was safe. She was at sea. But, God, how she hurt.

By nightfall, Christina didn't feel so safe anymore. Her whole face was swollen and masked with dried blood, and her forehead was on fire, burning with fever. The pain worsened. There was a chance, she realized, that she had broken a bone in her cheek, and she needed a doctor. She buried her head in the burlap and decided

that she no longer cared whether she lived or died. All she wanted was peace. She closed her eyes, and peace came to her.

Eleven hours passed before she opened her eyes again. It surprised her. She hadn't died after all. Well, Christina thought, if I'm going to live, and apparently I am, I might as well find somebody who can help me.

The pain had become unrelenting, and she had no intention of facing the real possibility of starvation.

How long had she been lying there?

One night?

Two?

Christina could no longer remember. She no longer cared.

She wanted out.

Now.

She had to get out.

Christina couldn't take the pain any longer.

She cautiously pulled herself to her feet and the pit began to spin viciously around her. Christina fell against the wall, pressing against it for support until the haze that had clouded her mind cleared away. Her body ached all over, and she wiped away the blood that had clotted around the corners of her mouth.

She stumbled against the iron rungs of a narrow ladder and slowly began to climb up out of the storage chamber, using every ounce of strength she had left. The metal cover had been shifted into place, but no one had locked it, and Christina shoved it aside. Sunlight splashed into her face, and she squinted against the brightness of the morning as it reflected off the ocean and spilled across the ship.

Christina tumbled onto the deck, losing her balance as the ship pitched its way roughly into the whitecaps that churned around its bow.

She stood, disoriented and confused, uncertain where to go, and she stared into the surprised face of a young crewman. He was as shocked as Christina. Instinctively, she turned to run, but the sailor cut off her flight and grabbed her arm, yelling, "Where the hell did you come from?"

Christina did not reply.

"Do you speak English?"

She turned toward him.

"My God," he said as he gently brushed the matted curls away from her bloodstained face, "What happened to you?"

Christina lowered her eyes.

"You're coming with me," the crewman ordered, and she made no effort to resist him.

The young sailor stopped beside the captain's quarters and hesitated before he knocked. Andy Anderson was still asleep. He had been up most of the night and didn't like to be awakened. Christina's captor had no choice.

He knocked. Then again.

Andy flung the door open, frantically tugging at his pants, reaching for his shoes. No one ever dared wake him up unless it was an emergency. His eyes were wide and red from lack of sleep, a stubble of whiskers covered his face.

"What's going on here?" he yelled. Andy saw Christina, and his body stiffened.

"I found her standing on deck," the crewman reported officially.

"Where?"

"Down beside the paint lockers."

A look of concern crept across Andy's face. He dismissed the sailor with the wave of his hand, and gently put his arm around Christina's waist. Her eyes were sunken, and her knees had begun to buckle. Andy caught her before she hit the floor and carried her across the room to his bunk.

In a very quiet voice, the captain said, "Chicken, you look terrible. What happened to you, and how on earth did you get aboard this ship?"

Christina tried to open her swollen eyes, and she said in a raspy voice, "You know how I came aboard, Andy. You invited me to dinner."

He frowned.

"You left," she continued, coughing. "John left. But I never left."

Andy brought her a glass of water. "Does John know you're on this ship?"

"John doesn't know a thing," Christina answered, her voice beginning to fade.

"You're a stowaway," the captain said firmly.

Christina nodded.

"You've broken the law."

Another nod. "I really don't care," she said. "I'm too ill to think straight. Please get somebody who can help me, Andy. I hurt so bad. I feel so bad." Christina's words drifted off. She groaned once and was asleep.

Andy tightened his jaws and patted her hand as it dangled lifelessly over the edge of the bunk. Christina was a helluva woman, he told himself. She had certainly gotten herself into a helluva fix. Andy winced as he looked down at the large purplish bruise spreading across her face like a distorted tattoo that had disfigured her beauty. He had almost finished washing the bloody film from around Christina's eyes by the time Doc Cunningham walked into the captain's quarters.

Andy stood quietly in the corner, watching and waiting while the ship's doctor deftly probed Christina's injuries. When the brief examination had been completed, the captain asked, "What's the diagnosis, Doc?"

"She banged herself up pretty good."

"Is it serious?"

"It could have been if you hadn't found her." Cunningham rolled down his sleeves and pitched his stethoscope back into the black broken leather satchel he always carried. "She's suffered some shock, and she has a pretty high fever, but I don't think she's broken any bones. I do suggest, however, that we get her to sick bay as soon as possible. What she needs more than anything else right now is a lot of rest." The doctor began fishing around in his bag. "What the hell was she doing on the ship anyway?"

Andy looked at him with a poker face.

Doc Cunningham understood and kept the rest of his questions to himself. He produced a handful of pills to fight infection and gave Christina a shot of morphine to end the pain that tormented her body.

She groaned again and looked up with drowsy eyes. The whole world seemed to be drifting past her, and Christina kept trying to reach out and keep it from leaving her behind. The faces staring down from above her were familiar but out of focus, and she heard them speak her name yet didn't know why. Nothing made sense anymore. She just wanted them to leave her alone, whoever they were, and Christina felt herself floating and free from pain at last.

Andy, aware that Christina had finally awakened, leaned down over her and asked slowly, "Who stowed you away?"

"Nobody did. I did it all by myself," she slurred.

Christina tried to smile and wondered why the out of focus face above her looked so harsh and hostile.

"Did John help you?" the face asked.

"John doesn't know anything."

She turned away, closed her eyes, watched the shadows clot the wall, dancing morosely in the sunlight.

"I don't know what you're talking about," Doc Cunningham said to the captain. "And I'm sure it's none of my bus'ness. But I'll tell you one thing. That girl's flat telling you the truth. She's too drugged up to lie to you.

Andy nodded, his face still expressionless. "You take care of the girl," he said. "I've got to go see a man about his wife."

John Christy was still sleeping when Captain Anderson knocked loudly on his door. He rolled out of his bunk, shook his head to rid himself of the cobwebs, and was rubbing his eyes as he staggered across the floor of his cabin. He opened the door and saw the face he expected to see. While off duty, no one ever awakened him unless something was amiss or had gone wrong. This time there was something different about the way Andy was staring at him. John didn't believe he had ever seen his captain wearing such a stern, solemn expression before, and he immediately braced himself for the worst.

Andy entered the cabin without a word and tossed his cap onto John's bunk. He seated himself, and his gaze cut deeply into his second officer as though trying to dissect the man's mind even before he spoke.

"We've got a stowaway aboard," Andy said.

John shrugged his shoulders. He didn't like being disturbed just to hear about some poor fool hiding away on the ship. In foreign ports, that happened all the time. Everybody in troubled times wanted to go to America. "That doesn't concern me," he replied.

"This time it does."

John's eyes narrowed.

"It's your wife."

The color drained from John's face, and he felt a sudden bolt of fear gouge into his stomach. It took a moment or two for him to recover.

"What's Christina doing aboard ship?" he asked.

"That's what I'd like for you to tell me," Andy answered grimly.

"Where is she?" John's voice was edged with anger and a measure of humiliation.

"In sick bay?"

"Is she hurt?"

"She's all right, John. But she's not a pretty sight."

"What happened to her?" John reached for his uniform shirt and kicked his shoes out from beneath his bunk.

Andy cleared his throat. "She stayed aboard after dinner the other night and, when nobody was looking, she jumped into a paint locker and messed her face up pretty good."

John was running down the corridor, Andy right behind him. "How is she?"

"Doc's got her knocked out with a shot, and he's putting ice on the swelling. She's got a little fever and is awfully dehydrated, but he's not worried about her."

"I am."

"You better be."

John stopped in his tracks and whirled around. "What do you mean by that?" he snapped.

"She's broken the law."

"She's my wife."

"That may make it hard on both on you."

John's voice softened. "Andy," he said, almost pleading, "you're my best friend."

"I'm also captain of this ship."

"Will there be an inquiry?"

"You're damn right there will be."

John rushed into sick bay just as Doc Cunningham had finished packing Christina's face in ice. The sight of her stunned him. The swelling had hideously deformed the way she looked, and the purplish bruise that encased her eyes had turned black, then green.

"My God," was all he could say.

"Don't worry," Doc said, "It's not permanent. In a week or two, she'll look just like she always did." He gave John a bemused look. "I knew you had taken a bride, John. I just didn't know you were taking her home with you."

"Neither did I, Doc." John sighed sharply, sat down on the edge of the bed, and repeated, "Neither did I."

"Why'd she do it?"

"She was upset, I guess. She was frustrated."

"And in love."

John grinned. "That, too," he said. "The Russians wouldn't let her leave, and it might be a year before I could get her out." He shrugged again. "Patience is not one of Christina's virtues."

"She's got a lot of guts," Doc said.

"She's crazy," Andy said, laughing for the first time.

"And she's lucky."

"How's that?" John asked.

"The paint locker is only fifteen feet deep. If she had jumped into another hole, it might have killed her."

John winced. "She is a little crazy," he agreed with Andy. "But Christina is a survivor. She's had to be." He glanced up at Doc Cunningham. "How long is she gonna be out," he asked.

"At least fourteen hours."

John reached down and gingerly touched Christina's sleeping face, then held her curls in his hand.

"I'll wait," he said.

Andy laid a firm hand on his second officer's shoulder. It was a gesture of understanding, of support. Then he left without a word.

Darkness had settled down around the ship by the time Christina opened her eyes. She saw John and blinked, and a wave of tempered fear swept over her. Her mouth went dry. She was so glad to see him again. But what must he think of her now.

Please, God, she prayed, just let him tell me that he still loves me.

John's eyes flickered in the dim light as he gradually became aware that Christina was finally awake. He stared down at her without smiling. And his tired voice was grating.

"Why the hell did you do such a dangerous thing?" he snapped at her.

Christina uttered a helpless cry of alarm, then her eyes were flecked with disappointment and anger. John's question, she thought, was absolutely absurd and it made her furious. "Get out of here," she growled. "If you don't know why I'm here, then you can just get away from me and get lost."

John took her in his arms and kissed her.

Christina's head throbbed, but she no longer cared.

"I'm sorry," he whispered, "but I've been worried sick about you. I looked everywhere for you. I thought you had run away, and I was afraid that I would never see you again."

"Kiss me one more time," Christina whispered.

John smiled, at ease with himself for the first time. "You sure look a mess," he told her. "But I love you anyway."

Thank you, God, Christina said softly to herself.

She looked up with a pained expression. "Are you in trouble, John?" she asked.

"No."

"That's good." Christina's smile was a crooked line across her swollen face. "That's all I worried about. I would do anything to be with you, John. But I would never do anything to hurt you."

He kissed her again and lay his face next to hers while she slept. Maybe she was foolish, he thought. Maybe she did do crazy, dangerous, things. She was sometimes impertinent, always impatient. But at least she was on her way to America. He laughed out loud and couldn't help it.

Chapter 19

CAPTAIN ANDERSON CALLED JOHN and Christina together into his office late during the fifth day of her recovery. The swelling had gone out of her face, and the bruise had slowly begun to fade. She was still weak and nauseous at times, though she blamed most of her misery on the ship as it rolled and pitched its way through the North Sea.

"We're approaching Dover, England," Andy said dourly. "I've had to notify authorities there that we have a stowaway on board."

John nodded. He knew the rules. He knew that Andy Anderson ran his ship by the book.

Christina lowered her eyes and looked nervously away.

"Ordinarily we wouldn't be stopping there at all," Andy explained to her, "but we had a cowboy break his leg pretty bad while we hauling the load of cattle to Poland. He's been in a hospital in Dover, and we'll be docking to pick him up."

"Will I be taken off the ship in Dover?" Christina asked, her voice fragile and unsure of itself.

"I don't know. It's up to the immigration authorities there." Andy paused, and his gaze swung back and forth from Christina to John. "I'd like to help both of you. You know that. I'd be willing to do anything within my power to get Christina safely to America. That's where she ought to be. That's the only place where she'll ever have a chance to find happiness." He stood and shrugged apologetically. "But I want you to know that I've officially asked Dover to take our stowaway off my hands."

"Do they know she's my wife?" John asked.

"I told them."

"Are they angry at John?" Christina wanted to know.

"They understand the situation. They may not like it, but they understand it."

"Thank you," she whispered.

"What happens if Immigration takes her at Dover?" John asked impatiently.

"Chances are, she'll be deported back to Poland."

"That's absurd."

"So is stowing away."

"You're not being fair, Andy," John spit out.

"I don't make the rules."

Christina had gambled. She was so sure that, this time, she and John would make it to America together. That had made the pain, the fear, the frustration all worthwhile. But now her dream was being shattered again. The decision would be made at Dover.

Dover lay two days away.

Christina and John walked hand in hand to the bow of the ship as the cold ocean wind bathed their faces with a stinging salt spray. For awhile both were silent, staring toward a horizon that hid the coast of England.

It seemed to Christina that she and John were always spending their last days, their last nights together, always saying goodbye, never knowing when or if they would ever find each other again. She had thought it would be different once they were married. She had been wrong.

Christina buried herself in John's arms.

They didn't have much. But they had each other.

And they had tonight.

For once, Christina dreaded the nights.

All they did were bring her closer to Dover and a final separation from John.

She couldn't hide from the nights.

But she found refuge from them as the ship bucked silently forward, and she and John wrapped themselves in the darkness and with each other.

The white cliffs rose up from the edge of a black sea and shimmered in the early morning sunlight. Christina had never seen anything quite so beautiful before, yet she stood quietly watching them through blurred eyes. She squeezed John's hand even tighter, as the tall, distinguished gentlemen, wearing a tweed overcoat, climbed stiffly aboard the ship. He would have to tear them apart, Christina told herself. He would have to drag her away, screaming and scratching and clawing. She was tired of always smiling humbly while someone else tried to run her life for her. The time had come to fight back.

Christina sighed.

She was also tired of lying to herself.

The English gentleman blew on his hands to warm them and waved amiably to Captain Anderson who was walking formally toward him. They chatted a few minutes, and the immigration official kept glancing toward Christina, frowning slightly, his sharp, pinched face devoid of any merriment. He was a dapper man, a black derby perched royally on his head, and his white mustache was long and neatly trimmed. But his eyes were cold. He was obviously a professional at handling awkward and adverse situations, a government man who, to

Christina, looked as though he had a heart as hard as flint.

He strolled toward her, tugging on his leather gloves. He bowed slightly as he took her hand.

"So you're the stowaway?" the official said.

"Yes." Her voice was barely audible.

"A lovely girl stowaway. Those are the best kind."

Christina forced a frightened smile.

"And you want to go to America?"

"Yes."

"To be with your husband, I understand."

Christina nodded.

He turned to John. "And you, I presume, are the fortunate groom."

John stood at attention. "Yes, sir." His reply, his appearance typified his military training.

"We have laws," the official said to Christina, "and I'm afraid that some of them don't seem very fair at times." He shrugged. "I can't change them. I can't make new ones." He laughed. "But I can sure ignore them anytime I damn well please."

He kissed Christina in a fatherly fashion on her cheek and shook John's hand.

"Good luck to both of you," he said.

Christina was flabbergasted.

"Then you're not going to take me off the ship?" she asked, her heart pounding, her pulse racing.

"Why should I?" The official laughed again. "You don't belong in England, my dear. You belong with him."

Christina wasn't sure she had heard the man correctly.

"You may find this hard to believe," he said jovially, "but I was in love once." He winked. "Some people think I still am."

With a cheery wave of his hand, the official turned and walked briskly back toward Captain Anderson. "We don't want her," he said loudly. "This is one stowaway you've got to handle yourself, Captain, although it looks like you may have someone to help you."

Christina glanced up at John. His laughter was rich and triumphant. Even Andy was beaming. The pressure had at last been taken from his shoulders.

It should be a time for celebration, she thought.

Then why did she feel so badly? A wave of nausea surged through her, and Christina doubled up with pain. She gagged and slumped in a crumpled heap upon the deck, coughing and gasping for breath, drowning in her own vomit.

For nine days, she lay in sick bay, as near death as she had ever felt in her life.

Doc Cunningham kept forcing food down her three times a day.

"That's just torture," John told him. "She throws up everything she eats."

"She's gonna be vomiting whether she eats or not, and if she doesn't have any food in there, it could very easily rupture her stomach."

"What's wrong with her?"

"I'm not for sure yet." The doc grinned. "But you'll know as soon as I do."

It didn't take him long to find out.

On the tenth morning of her sickness, the color had returned to Christina's face and she was breathing easier. The medicine Cunningham concocted for her had begun to take effect, and he even heard her laughter ringing through the infirmary for a change. Doc walked to her bedside and noticed that the faint hint of a sparkle had found its way back into her eyes. He sat down beside Christina and took her cold hand in his.

"Well," he said grinning, "it looks like you've decided to rejoin the race of the living after all."

"It's been pretty bad hasn't it?"

"I've seen worse."

Christina forced herself to sit up in bed and immediately began fluffing her curls.

"I must look terrible," she said.

"I've seen better."

"You're laughing at me." Christina faked a pout. "You shouldn't laugh at anybody who's been as seasick as I have. The ship was rolling so bad the other night, I just saw the salt and pepper shakers slide from one end of the table to the other and threw up until morning."

Doc leaned back in his chair and crossed his legs. "I've seen a lot of seasick sailors," he said. "I've seen them so sick they wanted to die. Hell, I've seen them so sick they tried to die. It's gotta be just about the most unpleasant feeling in the world."

Doc paused and glanced at the chart he had been carrying. He scratched his jaw, then leaned back at Christina and said slowly, "Honey, I don't know how to tell you this, but what you've got hasn't got a thing to do with bein' seasick."

"What's wrong?" she asked, suddenly alarmed.

"It's not what you'd call serious." He scratched his head, then his neck, hesitated, and finally said, "Let me try to put this as succinctly as possible. Christina, when was the last time you had your period?"

She blushed.

"June." It was a whisper.

"Hasn't that concerned you any?"

"No. I just thought that maybe when people get married, things like that stop for awhile."

Doc grinned broadly. "Sometimes they do, for about nine months or so."

Christina frowned. "What are you trying to tell me?" she asked.

"Honey," he replied, "let me be the first to congratulate you. The reason you've been so sick is that you're gonna have a baby."

"Oh, my God."

Christina slumped back in her bed and covered her face with both hands.

"I don't think I want to have a baby," she said.

"I'm afraid you don't have much of a choice."

She turned and looked at him sternly. "Can you take care of me."

"Sure." Doc Cunningham brushed his hair back. "I've had a lot of experience with pregnancies."

"On a ship full of men?"

Doc grinned again. "Oh, I'm usually not on a ship," he confided. "And generally I'm not around that many men." He shrugged matter-of-factly. "Mostly I'm a veterinarian. They brought me along to keep the cattle healthy. And, honey, those old heifers didn't give me nearly as many sleepless nights as you have."

"Who'll tell John?"

"I think that's a job that belongs to the mother."

Christina, for the first time in her life, didn't understand herself or her feelings. She was excited. She was scared. She was proud. She was depressed. It was both the happiest and saddest moment she had ever experienced. She was going to have a baby, and she felt like crying and laughing and throwing up again. Maybe it would be a boy, she thought, and, maybe, she would call him John.

The excitement was only momentary, then it died away, and Christina faced the truth. She had never been around children. She didn't understand children. She didn't particularly like children. She had never wanted children. What in the world was she going to do with a child?

Then she smiled to herself.

At least her child would be in America.

At least her child would be free.

The worst of Christina's days were behind her. The

nausea came and went, but it wasn't so severe anymore. She had finally accepted the fact that she was with child. John was elated. He now had everything he had ever hoped for. He was, he kept telling Christina, the happiest man on earth. Everything was perfect.

Even the seas were calm.

They were calm to everyone but Christina.

Ed Hanson, the radio officer, had volunteered to let Christina move into his cabin. "It's more than I need anyway," he said. "I just use it to sleep in, and I seldom have time to sleep anymore." He was in his fifties, married, the father of two children, and Ed Hanson would grin and say that he was kind of partial to children, born and unborn unlike. Christina needed her privacy. She could find it in his cabin. He dragged his cot into the radio room and settled down for the long voyage home.

Every night, when Christina retired for bed, Captain Anderson locked the door to her room. And she didn't leave in the morning until he had returned to unlock it.

"I think you're being foolish," she told him.

"You can't be too careful anymore."

"I'll be safe enough."

"Chicken," he said, placing a protective arm around her waist, "there's a lot of good men on this ship, but there's a lot of good men who haven't been around a woman in a long time. I've got sailors and cowboys and deck hands from countries you haven't even heard about. And I've seen them watching you, and I know what's going through their minds. You're never safe when you're alone."

"But I'm pregnant."

Andy grinned. "It doesn't make them any difference."

"But I'm ugly."

"Not yet you aren't."

"I still think you're silly."

"Hell, Christina," Andy roared. "When are you gonna learn the rules of this ship. Nobody argues with the captain." He nudged her playfully into the cabin and locked the door.

She was still yelling when he turned the corner at the far end of the corridor and made his way to the bridge.

Nights were rough for her.

The sea didn't cooperate. It kept pitching Christina out of her bunk, throwing her onto the floor. She was tired. She was bruised. She spent the rest of most nights sleeping in a chair.

Christina complained once to Andy.

He laughed and paid her no attention.

She complained again.

He came to her cabin that night, his arm draped with every loose belt he could confiscate.

"What are you going to do with those?" she asked.

"Lay down," the captain ordered.

She obeyed, and he belted her into the bunk. Christina couldn't move very well. She couldn't turn over. She wasn't comfortable at all.

But she didn't hit the floor that night.

Andy Anderson never heard her complain again.

Every evening, when the winds weren't too bitter, the spray too biting, Christina, dressed in a hand-me-down khaki uniform, dutifully climbed to the top deck and waited until John finished his watch at four o'clock. It was their time to be together, a time for discovery about each other and about themselves. Their courtship had been a savage whirlwind. They had married as strangers. Now, far from the reaches of civilization, stranded amidst the barbarous waves of the Atlantic Ocean, they learned to like each other, respect each other, accept each other for who and what they were.

Christina was a maverick.

John was the responsible one.

She loved medicine.

He loved the sea.

She was mischievous.

He was a romantic.

She hated housework.

He would never leave the sea.

Christina loved life.

The sea was John's life.

She hated being left alone.

The sea would forever keep them apart.

Christina sighed.

It would be hard, she said. The nights would be long and lonesome. But she would wait for him.

Aboard ship, John was a different person, devoted to his duty. His job always came first. Nothing could distract him, not even Christina, not even his thoughts of a child.

Christina, her voice almost lost in the sound of crashing waves, confessed she was a spoiled brat.

John, too, had a confession to make.

There was discomfort in his eyes. His complexion darkened noticeably.

My God, Christina wondered, what's he going to tell me now. Is he married? Has he been married? Is he divorced? A good Catholic woman couldn't tolerate such a fate. Had he lied to her?

"I haven't told my mother that we're married," he said.

"Why not? Are you ashamed of me?"

"No, Christina, of course not. It's just that I didn't want to do it by telephone. That seemed so cold. And I didn't want to tell her in a letter. That seemed a little too impersonal." He hugged Christina tightly, sheltering her from the frosty spray that the wind tossed in their faces. "I thought we could do it together."

"I hope she likes me."

John smiled but didn't answer.

So do I, he said to himself.

They held each other and braced themselves against the cold September gales of the Atlantic while the whales and the flying fish escorted them on across a restless sea toward America and home.

Christina was standing on the bridge in the haze of early morning when she caught her first faint glimpse of the Virginia coast. It mesmerized her. She leaned against the railing, virtually breathless, and watched the port of Norfolk growing larger, coming toward her, as the ship eased through the mist, impatient men working in a frenzy all around her as they prepared to dock.

America.

She said the word softly to herself and felt the tears begin to well up in her eyes.

America.

She had waited so long. There had been so many times when she didn't think this moment would ever happen.

America.

It was for her. It was for her baby.

The home of the brave.

The land of the free.

As the *Robert W. Hurt* docked, Christina saw two men with grim, unsmiling faces following Captain Anderson as they all walked toward her.

There was something about them that frightened her, and she didn't quite know why.

"Are you Christina Christy?" the man in the brown suit asked her.

"Yes." She glanced at Andy. "But you must know that."

"Then come with us, please."

Concern furrowed her brow. "Who are you?" she questioned.

"We're with the Immigration Department."

"What do you want with me?"

"You're a stowaway." The man in the brown suit was all business. He had not yet looked at her in the eye.

"I'm married to an officer on this ship."

"Do you have a marriage certificate?"

"Yes."

"Get it, please."

In her cabin, Christina nervously rummaged through her purse until she found the certificate. She turned and handed it to the man in the brown suit.

"It's signed by the priest," he said.

"He's the one who married us."

"It's not signed by the Polish government."

Christina froze.

"It's not legal," he said. "Do you have a passport?"

"Yes."

She produced it for him, holding her breath while he quickly thumbed through its pages.

He glanced up. "Do you have an exit visa from the Russian government in Poland?"

"No."

The man in the brown suit shrugged without emotion. "Then we'll have to arrest you as an illegal immigrant." He pulled a set of metal handcuffs from his coat pocket and clamped them roughly on her wrists.

Christina looked frantically at Andy. "Where's John?"

"I'll get him." The captain patted her shoulder and winked to reassure her. "I'm sure this is just a formality," he said.

"I don't understand what's happening," she protested. "I'm being hauled off the ship like a common criminal."

"Don't worry. They'll treat you decently." He grinned. "After all, this is America, not Russia."

So it was.

America.

Christina mumbled the word again.

America.

The home of the brave.

The land of the free.

"Where are you taking her?" Andy asked the man in the brown suit.

"To the Norfolk Prison Farm," he said and pushed Christina out the door and into the corridor of what had been her liberty ship.

Chapter 20

THE PRISON FARM OUTSIDE NORFOLK was as cold and austere as the December morning. The day had dawned gray and had not improved, and there was, the radio said, threats of another snow before nightfall. The clouds clustered thick and heavy overhead, and a brisk wind slapped Christina in the face as she and a gray-haired, kindly-faced federal marshall left the compound and began the long ride to her hall of justice.

"Are you going to put handcuffs on me again?" she asked timidly.

The marshall grinned as he glanced down at her stomach. It was beginning to swell. "I don't think you're gonna run off anywhere and leave me, are you," he said.

"I don't think I can."

"Then there's no reason for you to be wearing any of my bracelets," he drawled. "I don't think they would look too good on you anyway."

"Thank you."

He opened the car door for her, and they drove away from Christina's white stucco dormitory, stopping beside the high steel wire fence long enough for a heavy-set officer wrapped warmly in a black woolen coat, a huge pistol strapped on his waist, to run out of his cozy wooden guardhouse and unlock the gate.

He waved.

The marshall nodded and turned his car toward town.

Christina glanced over her shoulder at the sprawling compound that had been her home for the last four months. All she could see were those dreaded bars on the windows and the smiling, hopeful face of Irene Bergman. Christina didn't believe she could have made it without her.

Irene served as head matron for the prison farm. She was blonde, had blue eyes, was in her late forties, and, like Christina, spoke with a distinct foreign accent.

She had been appalled the day Christina was brought to the farm, a wisp of a girl, frightened and in a strange land, shackled with handcuffs.

"This one's a special case," the man in the brown suit had said in his raspy, monotone voice.

"What has she done?" Irene had asked softly.

"She's an illegal immigrant." He removed the handcuffs and stepped back, squaring his shoulders. "She is not to see a clergyman, she is not to see a doctor until the Immigration Department decides what it wants to do with her."

"I'm pregnant," Christina said. It was almost a whisper.

"She's not to see a doctor," the man in the brown suit repeated.

"That's a little harsh isn't it?" Irene Bergman asked, her hands on her hips.

"That's my orders." The man in the brown suit cut his eyes sharply toward the head matron. "Those are your orders."

"I don't like them."

"You're not paid to like them. You're paid to follow them." He turned on his heels and walked out of the room, the door slamming shut behind him.

Irene put a comforting arm around Christina's waist. "Don't be frightened," she said. "I'll do what I can for you." She grinned, and her eyes shone brightly. "You see, I understand. I'm an immigrant, too."

"From where?" Christina smiled for the first time. In America, she had found a friend.

"Sweden. That was twenty years ago, and I still remember that magic moment when I finally set my feet on this good old American soil." Irene suddenly laughed as though something funny had struck her. "I don't guess you will ever forget either, will you?"

Christina laughed with her.

She had spent those four months in a sparsely furnished dormitory room with eight beds and eight delinquent teenage girls. They looked upon Christina as a celebrity. They were only guilty of running away from home and finding some drunken sailor from the nearby U.S. Navy Base to sleep with on the weekends. But Christina had survived a war, been smuggled past the Russians, defied the Polish government, and stowed away on a ship that carried her halfway around the worlds. She had slept with a good looking sailor, too, but only after she had married him.

She sometimes felt like an old mother hen looking after a bunch of loud, unpredictable, raucous, and usually lovable little chicks.

She hated to see one of the girls brought to the prison farm. But Christina always missed her when she was gone. She was allowed to cook her own meals, and it was a chore she feared.

"I don't know how to cook," Christina confided to Irene.

"You're married," she was told. "It's time you learned."

"I can't."

Irene Bergman pitched the pots and pans at her feet and walked stubbornly out of the room.

For weeks, Christina lived on eggs and soup.

When John came, and he came at least three times a week, he brought new skirts and blouses, books and magazines, pineapples and peanut butter, and sometimes even a box of candy.

He was the only outsider permitted to see her.

When Irene Bergman saw John standing at the doorway, she always found a convenient reason to excuse herself, bend a few rules, and leave them alone in the sitting room.

The *Robert W. Hurt* was being sold to a company in France. At the moment, John was restricted to shore duty. For him and Christina, it couldn't have come at a better time.

On the night before Thanksgiving, Christina awoke in a cold sweat. Her face burned with fever, and her head kept throbbing, and it even hurt to rub her eyes. She sat up in bed, and an old feeling of nausea grumbled inside her. Christina barely made it to the bathroom before she threw up. The pain lodged in the pit of her stomach, and all she could think about was the baby.

She vomited again, and her whole body was twisted and wracked with convulsions.

The baby.

Her head pounded to the rhythm of her pulse beat.

She couldn't lose the baby.

Irene Bergman found her lying in the floor, her eyes wide with fear, clutching her stomach.

"I've got to get a doctor for you," she said, kneeling.

"They said I can't see a doctor."

"To hell with them."

"It's the rules."

"To hell with the rules."

The nurse at the medical dispensary was cautious. "If we call a doctor, it may cost us our jobs," she argued.

"If we don't, it may cost this girl her baby."

"I'm not gonna take the responsibility by myself."

"You don't have to," Irene snapped. "I'm here. Now call him and be quick about it."

It was past midnight when the doctor arrived. He treated Christina for intestinal flu, giving her an IV to prevent any possibility of dehydration.

"She'll be all right now," he said, "but she's had it pretty rough."

"If you only knew," Irene said, laughing.

"I'm probably better off if I don't."

Irene Bergman paid him out of her own pocket. It was expensive, but it was better that way. Now there would be no incident to report, no papers to file. No one would ever know she had kept bending the rules until they finally broke.

John tried to repay her.

Irene refused.

"Just get her out of this place," she said. "She doesn't belong here. She has no business here. Use your money, for God's sake, to get her out."

John nodded. He was trying.

An attorney, rumored to be the best in Norfolk, had accepted their case, and his assistant sat with Christina late one afternoon, carefully explaining the papers he had asked her to sign.

There were so many of them.

None made a lot of sense.

But she had to put her trust in somebody.

Christina looked up as Joseph L. Morgan, esquire, the head of immigration stalked without knocking into the room. He was in his late fifties and stared at her through steel gray eyes. He was a small man, only about five feet and five inches in stature, and Christina had the immediate impression that he probably didn't like people, but loved his job and the authority it gave him. He made it a point to never smile.

The young attorney stood to face him. "What do you want?" he asked.

"I've come for Mrs. Christina Christy," he said.

"May I ask why?"

Morgan frowned, removed his glasses, and folded his arms defiantly. He certainly didn't like being questioned by anyone so young and apparently impudent.

"Who the hell are you?"

"Mrs. Christy's attorney."

Morgan rubbed his mouth with the back of his hand. He was silent for a moment, studying the situation, then spoke. "We have decided to transfer her from here to Ellis Island, then deport her back to Poland."

The attorney grinned. "You can't."

"Who the hell's gonna stop me?"

"The court."

Morgan's eyes narrowed on his pallid, pinched face.

The young attorney waved the papers in his face. "The hearing has been set for the sixth of December," he said. He glanced back at Christina, then added with a caustic grin, "You can't touch her."

"We'll see." Morgan's voice was like gravel. His face reddened. It was a threat.

Now, on this bleak December morning, Christina would be facing Joseph L. Morgan, esquire, again.

In court.

It was a place Morgan knew well. He spent a lot of time before a lot of judges. He liked to brag that he had never lost a case.

Never. He had already booked passage for Christina Christy back to Poland.

The federal marshall's car eased to a stop outside the

courthouse. The clouds had gotten heavier, the day grayer. Outside her window, Christina saw John and her attorney, Thomas Blackburn, standing in the cold and waiting for her. Their breaths were frosted, and the wind seemed to be blowing harder than before. They moved as one toward her, and Blackburn waved jovially to the marshall.

The attorney was an imposing man, taller than six feet and weighing more than two hundred pounds. He had a voice to match his size, deep and resonant. Blackburn was wearing a dark blue suit and matching striped tie, carrying an attache case. He pulled a gold watch from his vest pocket and glanced at it.

"We've got fifteen minutes until the hearing," he announced. He shook Christina's hand, then held it tightly. "Well, my dear," he said, "today is the day you have your first taste of freedom in America."

"How do you know?"

Blackburn winked. "Trust me," he said. "Within the next thirty minutes, you will be walking out of here in the protective custody of your husband."

"Are you sure?" Christina had heard promises before, and most of them had been empty ones. She was afraid to hope.

"I guarantee it." Blackburn's voice was booming.

"But I've been told that Morgan has never lost a case before."

Blackburn laughed. "He can say that this morning," the attorney told her, "but he won't be able to say it this afternoon. He fouled this case up something horrible. He hasn't allowed you to see a doctor. He hasn't permitted you to see a preacher or a priest of any kind. And, hell, Christina, even hardened criminals have those privileges. I don't know what he's got against you, girl, but he's fighting you out of sheer spite."

"I hope the judge agrees," John said as the three of them walked into the warmth of the courthouse.

"Morgan's tactics throughout this whole ordeal have been downright inhumane. The judge won't stand for them."

"How do you know?"

"The judge is a fair man." Blackburn grinned. "Besides, he and I play golf together every Thursday when it's not too cold, and it wasn't very cold last Thursday." The attorney shrugged. "Of course, the judge doesn't always listen or agree with me. But he damn well listens to his wife, and she plays bridge with my wife, and my wife don't like what's happened worth a damn."

Morgan brushed past them, cocky as always, his gray eyes dancing. He loved his days in court. He hesitated before entering the courtroom, and turned back toward Christina.

"Well, Mrs. Christy," he announced loudly, "you've eluded me long enough. By tonight, you'll be on your way to Ellis Island, and we'll have one less immigrant to worry about around here."

His laughter was hollow.

Christina's face was flushed.

Blackburn simply looked over at John and said softly, "That stupid son of a bitch."

In court, Blackburn asked simple but direct questions.

"Christina is pregnant. Why wasn't she allowed to see a doctor?"

There was no answer.

"Christina is a devout Catholic. Why hasn't she been allowed to see a priest?"

Morgan shuffled through his notes.

"What crime has Christina committed, other than wanting to be with her husband and having her child born in the United States of America."

Morgan's jaws clenched. He stood silent, waiting for his turn to attack.

The judge leaned back and pondered Blackburn's questions, then he had a few of his own.

"What does the Immigration Department intend to do with Mrs. Christy?"

"Deport her to Poland," Blackburn answered before Morgan could speak.

The judge turned to the immigration official and asked, "Is that true?"

"Basically it is, your honor," Morgan replied. "It is our fundamental contention—"

The judge interrupted him with a wave of his hand. "What will happen to Mrs. Christy if she returns to Poland?" he wanted to know.

"She will be shot on the spot," Blackburn replied.

"Why?"

"She's considered a traitor by the Russian government which now runs the country."

"So the Russians want her?" the judge asked, surprised.

"That's right, your honor."

"And they want to shoot her."

"Yes, sir."

"And we haven't really treated her very well since she came to America have we?"

"No, sir." Blackburn glanced sideways at Morgan and swallowed the grin that was threatening to break out on his face.

The judge leaned forward and grew stern. "Deportation denied," he bellowed. "I'm placing Mrs. John Christy in the protective custody of her husband. Court adjourned."

Morgan, red-faced, threw his papers into his black attache case, glowered at Christina, then stormed out the big, walnut paneled double doors.

In the corridor outside the courtroom, Blackburn grew serious. He told John, "It's not necessarily over for you. The Immigration Department can keep reviewing the case for as long as it wants. Your basic problem is this:

the immigration boys do not accept your marriage because you have no certificate from the Polish government. In their eyes, it's not legal, and they're probably right."

"So what can we do about it?" John asked.

"That's simple." Blackburn began walking away. "You ought to be able to figure that one out without paying me to do it for you."

Darkness had settled gently upon Virginia, and a light snow was drifting across the woodlands.

Outside, a cold, biting wind was whistling through the trees as John and Christina Christy stood before a country justice of the peace and repeated their vows.

There was neither pomp nor circumstances, no candles, no flowers, no music, just a middle-aged stranger with a bible in his hand who asked the same questions he had asked so many times before.

"Do you promise to love?

"Honor?

"Cherish?"

Forever.

"I do," John said.

"I do," Christina echoed.

The justice of the peace smiled pleasantly, nodded to John, and said, "Now you can kiss the bride."

John grinned.

"I've done that a long time ago," he said.

But he did it again, and Christina clung to him, gently laughing and crying, and for a moment, she thought she felt their child move.

She had been married in the sight of God. Now she was married in the sight of man. She hoped God would understand and not hold it against her.

It was all over.

It was just beginning.

Christina licked a snowflake from her lips as she and John ran through the December night and lost themselves in the fragile warmth of another kiss.

EPILOGUE

A year later, Christina Christy, as the law required her to do, was driven from her mother-in-law's home in Portland, Maine, to the region's immigration department. She had a report to file, and it frightened her.

She had seen the cold steel eyes of immigration authorities before, and Christina remembered Morgan's harsh vow to deport her to Poland, no matter how many years of legal maneuvering it took him.

She thought of the Russians who would be waiting for her, and Christina shuddered.

Inside the small New England office, an elderly gentleman with thinning white hair glanced up from his paper work as Christina walked in. She briefly told her story and held her breath.

The immigration officer's brow furrowed as he heard her name. He pursed his lips and leaned forward, resting his elbows on the old mahogany desk. For a moment, he did not speak a word as he diligently studied her face, his eyes darting to the squirming baby boy she held in her arms.

"Now let me see if I've got all of this right," he said, rubbing his stubbled chin. "You are the wife of an American born husband?"

"Yes, sir."

"And you are the mother of an American born child?"

"Yes, sir."

The elderly man smiled as he shrugged. "So what's the problem?" he asked.

Christina smiled with him.

The elderly man stood and took the baby boy from her, cradling him in his arms, and carrying John Christy, Jr., as he followed Christina outside into a crisp Maine December morning.

The problem, she knew, was at last behind her.

Nine years after her arrival to the shores of America, Christina Christy became a United States Citizen.

For twenty-five years, she and John Christy remained happily married, raising four children: John Jr., Timothy, Kimberly, and Christopher.

For them, they had found, amidst the ashes and heartbreak of World War II, a romance that would last them a lifetime.

Only the sea ever kept them apart. And on the afternoon of February 1, 1972, when the *V.A. Fogg* went down off Galveston, it separated them, but not their love, for a final time.